Journeyman Electrician's Exam Workbook

based on the
2008 NEC®
National Electrical Code®

AMERICAN TECHNICAL PUBLISHERS, INC.
HOMEWOOD, ILLINOIS 60430-4600

R. E. Chellew

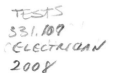
3 1257 01910 6474

Journeyman Electrician's Exam Workbook Based on the 2008 NEC® contains procedures commonly practiced in industry and the trade. Specific procedures vary with each task and must be performed by a qualified person. For maximum safety, always refer to specific manufacturer recommendations, insurance regulations, specific job site and plant procedures, applicable federal, state, and local regulations, and any authority having jurisdiction. The material contained is intended to be an educational resource for the user. American Technical Publishers, Inc. assumes no responsibility or liability in connection with this material or its use by any individual or organization.

Acknowledgments

The author and publisher are grateful to the following companies, organizations, and individuals for providing software, photographs, information, and technical assistance.

Pinella County Construction Licensing Board

Adobe, Acrobat, and Reader are either registered trademarks or trademarks of Adobe Systems Incorporated in the United States and/or other countries. Quick Quiz and Quick Quizzes are registered trademarks of American Technical Publishers, Inc. Intel and Pentium are registered trademarks of Intel Corporation or its subsidiaries in the United States and other countries. Microsoft, Windows, Windows NT, Windows XP, and Internet Explorer are either registered trademarks or trademarks of Microsoft Corporation in the United States and/or other countries. Netscape is a registered trademark of Netscape Communications Corporation in the United States and other countries. National Electrical Code and NEC are registered trademarks of the National Fire Protection Association, Inc., Quincy, MA 02269.

 made in USA

Contents

1 The Examination

1

Journeyman Electrician's Examination • Application and Examination Fees • Acceptance • Reference Books • Amendments • Private Testing Agencies • Special Examinations • School/Bookstores • Test Preparation • Test Grading • Test Structure • What to Take to the Examination • Grade Notification • Reciprocity

2 Definitions

15

Definitions • Accessible • Ampacity • Approved • Attachment Plug • Bonding • Bonding Jumper • Branch Circuit • Building • Continuous Load • Dwelling Unit • Electric Sign • Energized • Exposed • Feeder • Fitting • Grounded • Grounded Conductor • Grounded Conductor, Equipment • Guarded • Hoistway • In Sight • Interrupting Rating • Labeled • Nonlinear • Overcurrent • Qualified Person • Raintight • Receptacle Outlet • Service Drop • Service Lateral • Show Window • Special Permission • Thermal Protector • Voltage, Nominal • Wateright

3 Electrical Formulas

25

Ohm's Law • Current Calculation • Voltage Calculation • Resistance Calculation • Power Formula • Power Calculation • Series Circuit • Parallel Circuits • Series/Parallel Circuits • Horsepower • Efficiency Motors • Transformers • Transformer Efficiency • Ratio • Temperature Conversion • Converting Fahrenheit to Celsius • Converting Celsius to Fahrenheit • Busbar Calculations • Voltage Drop • Cost of Energy • Transposing Formulas • Metrics • English/Metric Conversion Factors •

4 NEC® Examples 47

Conduit Fill • Conductor Adjustment Factor • Temperature Correction • Single Motors • Full Load Current • Conductor Size • Overloads • Overload Protection • Disconnecting Means • Motor Feeders • Ranges (Household) • Calculating Box Fill for Conductors • Conductor Resistance • Electric Welders • Service Calculations • Service Load Calculations

5 Review Questions 69

6 Sample Licensing Exams 103

Sample Licensing Examinations • Examination Preparation

CD-ROM Contents

- *Using this CD-ROM*
- *Quick Quizzes®*
- *Illustrated Glossary*
- *Media Clips*
- *ATPeResources.com*

Journeyman Electrician's Exam Workbook Based on the 2008 NEC® is designed to help test applicants prepare for the Journeyman Electrician's Exam. The workbook is based on the 2008 National Electrical Code® and assumes that the student has a basic understanding of electrical theory and trade knowledge.

The Examples, Review Questions, and Sample Licensing Exams provide practice reviewing and answering questions similar to the questions on the Journeyman Electrician's Exam. Chapters 5 and 6 are timed to simulate test conditions. The workbook contains Review Question answers and NEC® references. Answers and NEC® references for all Sample Licensing Exam questions are given in the *Answer Key*.

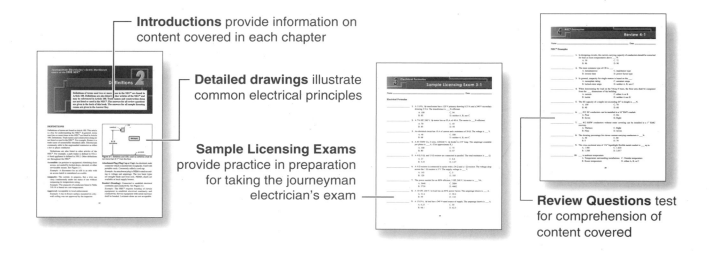

Introductions provide information on content covered in each chapter

Detailed drawings illustrate common electrical principles

Sample Licensing Exams provide practice in preparation for taking the journeyman electrician's exam

Review Questions test for comprehension of content covered

- Calculations resulting in a fraction less than 0.5 are permitted to be dropped per Annex D of the NEC®, Examples.

- Calculations for range loads, using the Standard Calculation or the Optional Calculation, resulting in a fraction less than 0.5 kW are permitted to be dropped per Annex D of the NEC®, Examples.

- Calculations for conductors all having the same cross-sectional area and the same insulation resulting in 0.8 or larger are rounded to the next higher number per Note 7 of Notes to Tables, Ch 9.

- Fine Print Notes are explanatory or provide additional information. For example, Section 90.6 discusses Formal Interpretation and explains where formal interpretation procedures may be found. The word "shall" indicates a mandatory rule.

Additional related educational materials are available from ATP. To obtain information about related training products, visit the ATP web site at www.go2atp.com.

The Publisher

Journeyman Electrician's Exam Workbook
based on the 2008 NEC®

Workbook CD-ROM

The *Journeyman Electrician's Exam Workbook Based on the 2008 NEC®* CD-ROM in the back of the book is designed as a self-study aid to enhance text content. The CD-ROM includes Quick Quizzes®, an Illustrated Glossary, Media Clips, and an ATPeResources.com button. Instructions for using the CD-ROM can be found on the last page of this book.

- The Quick Quizzes® provide an interactive review of fundamental concepts covered in the chapters.
- The Illustrated Glossary provides a helpful reference for key terms included in the text. Selected terms are linked to illustrations that enhance the provided definitions.
- The Media Clips contain video clips and animated graphics that depict electrical/electronic principles.
- ATPeResources.com provides a comprehensive array of instructional resources, including Internet links to manufacturers, associations, and ATP resources.

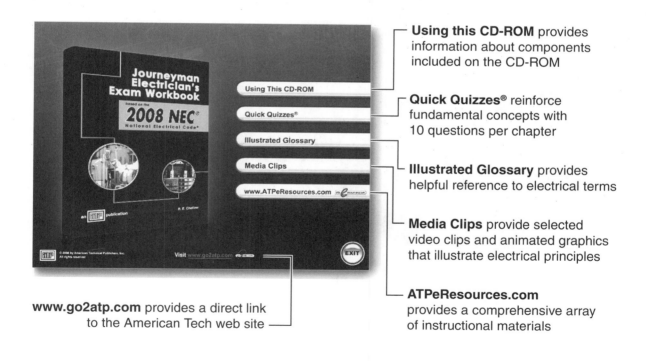

Using this CD-ROM provides information about components included on the CD-ROM

Quick Quizzes® reinforce fundamental concepts with 10 questions per chapter

Illustrated Glossary provides helpful reference to electrical terms

Media Clips provide selected video clips and animated graphics that illustrate electrical principles

ATPeResources.com provides a comprehensive array of instructional materials

www.go2atp.com provides a direct link to the American Tech web site

Also Available from ATP...

Journeyman Electrician's Exam Preparation CD-ROM is a stand-alone CD-ROM with 500 sample journeyman licensing exam questions in Microsoft® PowerPoint® presentation format that are used to prepare for the Journeyman Electrician's Exam.

The CD-ROM is designed for both self-study and classroom presentations. Questions are based on typical exams given by national testing agencies, and topics covered include electrical theory, trade knowledge, and 2008 NEC® references.

The **Exam Timer** is used to monitor the time allotted to complete a specific exam.

The **Answer Sheet** provides a printable document to easily record answers to the exam questions.

Sample Exam Questions are based on typical exams given by national testing agencies.

Highlighted Answers provide the correct response to the Practice Exam and to Exams 1 through 4.

NEC® References provide reference to specific exam question information in the National Electrical Code®.

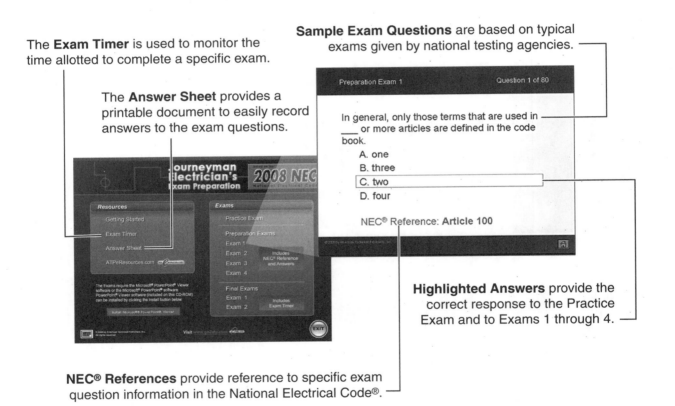

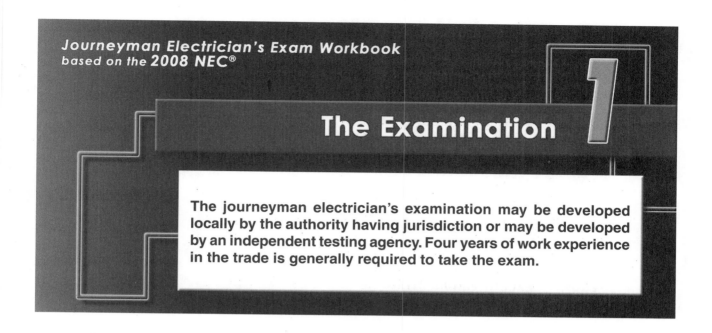

Journeyman Electrician's Exam Workbook
based on the 2008 NEC®

The Examination 1

The journeyman electrician's examination may be developed locally by the authority having jurisdiction or may be developed by an independent testing agency. Four years of work experience in the trade is generally required to take the exam.

JOURNEYMAN ELECTRICIAN'S EXAMINATION

The type of work and duties of a journeyman electrician are generally determined by local and state jurisdiction. The journeyman electrician usually performs electrical work under the supervision of a master electrician.

The journeyman electrician's examination consists of questions and problems prepared and administered by the local licensing board. Most local examinations are given periodically at a time and place specified by the examining board. Some licensing boards administer the test in parts, which are graded separately. Request a test breakdown when making application.

The electrical board establishes requirements of eligibility of applicants for the journeyman electrician's examination. The applicant is usually required to show four years experience in the electrical trade. Eligible applicants are administered a test to determine if they have the knowledge to perform electrical work on the journeyman level. The quality of their work must meet the requirements of local and national codes. It must be a safe electrical installation.

Applicants who pass the journeyman electrician's examination are issued a journeyman card. The card contains the name of the licensing board, the name of the cardholder, license number, expiration date, and issuance date. See Figure 1-1.

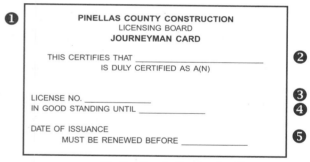

❶ AUTHORITY HAVING JURISDICTION

❷ CARDHOLDER

❸ LICENSE NUMBER

❹ EXPIRATION DATE

❺ ISSUANCE DATE

Figure 1-1. Applicants who pass the journeyman electrician's examination are issued a journeyman card by the authority having jurisdiction in the area.

Application and Examination Fees

Cover letters containing general information regarding the journeyman electrician's examination forms are usually provided by the licensing board. See Figure 1-2. Information in such cover letters may include:

• Signature and notarization required

1

- Type of examination
- Examination preparer
- Material that may be brought to examination

- Length of examination
- Minimum passing grade
- Cost of examination

Pinellas County Construction Licensing Board

ALL FEES ARE NONREFUNDABLE

TO: **APPLICANTS FOR JOURNEYMAN EXAMINATION**
FROM: **EXECUTIVE DIRECTOR**
REF: **CHAPTER 75-489, LAWS OF FLORIDA**

Each applicant must complete the attached application with supporting documents and file it with this office not later than _____. Applications must be signed and notarized as indicated. ❹

❶ Examinations are "open-book" and prepared for the PCCLB by an independent testing agency. Questions are multiple-choice, fill-in or true-false.

❷ All books and references must be brought by the examinee. No class notes, scratch paper, exam study aids or like materials will be allowed. Silent, battery-powered, non-printing calculators are permitted, and applicants must bring their own pencils, pens and rulers.

❸ Most examinations take about six hours with a lunch break of approximately one hour. Smoking is prohibited in the examination area. A passing grade is 70%. You will be notified of your grade within 30 days. **Do not call the PCCLB office before 30 days for your examination results.** ❺

If an applicant for an original certificate does not provide a complete application with all required supplementary information within one year from the date of filing the application, the fee paid shall be credited to the PCCLB as an earned fee. A new application for a certificate shall be accompanied by another application fee.

All experience requirements must be verified on attachment B. The form may be reproduced as needed and all verification must be notarized.

Application Fee . . . . $50.00 ❻

Suite 102   11701 Belcher Road   Largo, Florida 33773   Telephone (727) 536-4720

Pinellas County Construction Licensing Board

❶ **TYPE OF EXAMINATION**
❷ **MATERIAL THAT MAY BE BROUGHT**
❸ **LENGTH OF EXAM**
❹ **SIGNATURE AND NOTARIZATION REQUIRED**
❺ **MINIMUM PASSING GRADE**
❻ **COST OF EXAMINATION**

Figure 1-2. Cover letters contain information regarding the journeyman electrician's examination.

Forms detailing guidelines for experience may also be provided by the licensing board. Generally, four years of work experience in the trade, under the direction of an electrical contractor or master electrician, is required for eligibility to take the journeyman electrician's examination. Partial credit may be given for military service, school courses, and other related work experience. See Figure 1-3. Information in such forms may include:

Pinellas County Construction Licensing Board

TO: ALL ELECTRICAL JOURNEYMAN APPLICANTS
FROM: ELECTRICAL EXAMINING COMMITTEE
SUBJECT: GUIDELINES FOR EXPERIENCE

The subject guidelines should be used in determining your eligibility for journeyman licensure. Fees are non-refundable so make sure you have sufficient verified experience.

❶
1. You <u>must</u> have <u>four years verified</u> experience.

2. At least TWO of the four years required must be under the discretion of a properly licensed electrical contractor or master electrician.

3. Partial credit <u>may</u> be given for certain trade-related experience and education as follows, at the direction of the examining committee.
  ❹

❷
  a. <u>Military</u>
     Only actual time worked at the electrical trade with a <u>maximum of two years</u>. Must submit DD214.

❸
  b. <u>Trade School</u>
     One-half full time attendance with a <u>maximum of two years</u>.

  c. <u>Electrical Wholesale</u>
     <u>Maximum six months</u> credit.

  d. <u>Plant Maintenance/Municipal/Public Utility</u>
     Only actual time in the electrical trade with a <u>maximum of two years</u>.

  e. <u>Office/Condo Maintenance or Low Voltage Systems</u>
     <u>Maximum three months</u> credit.

  f. <u>Line Voltage Control Systems</u>
     <u>Maximum six months credit</u>.
     ❺

  g. <u>Marine Electrical Construction</u>
     <u>Maximum six months credit</u>.

  h. <u>Marine Electricians Mate (Licensed)</u>
     <u>Maximum two years credit</u>.

Suite 102 • 11701 Belcher Road • Largo, Florida 33773 • Telephone (727) 536-4720

Pinellas County Construction Licensing Board

❶ **4 YEARS OF WORK EXPERIENCE**
❷ **MILITARY SERVICE**
❸ **SCHOOL COURSES**
❹ **PARTIAL CREDIT**
❺ **RELATED WORK EXPERIENCE (c–h)**

Figure 1-3. Four years of work experience in the trade is generally required to take the journeyman electrician's examination.

- Minimum years of trade experience required
- Conditions of trade experience
- Partial credit

The journeyman application form contains spaces for the applicant to provide the information required by the licensing board. The licensing board requires that the applicant complete the journeyman application form and pay an examination fee. The information required will vary somewhat from jurisdiction to jurisdiction. See Figure 1-4. Generally, however, the following is required:

- Type of certificate applied for
- Personal information (address, telephone, etc.)
- Schools attended
- Employment
- Letters of reference
- Signature and notarization

Certificates in support of journeyman applicant's experience qualifications may also be required. See Figure 1-5. Such certifications must be made by former employers licensed as contractors. The certificate contains:

- Dates of employment
- Statement of applicant's experience
- Signature of employer
- Notarization

The licensing board generally accepts copies of your IRS W-2 form to verify work experience. The W-2 form may be used in cases where your ex-employer is no longer in business or cannot be located.

Acceptance

Upon fulfilling the requirements of the licensing board you will receive confirmation of a test date. This includes the location and time of the examination. The journeyman electrician's examination is generally given once a month. Jurisdictions may vary. Confirm availability for testing dates with your local licensing board.

Reference Books

The licensing board usually furnishes a list of books and study aids permitted in the examination room. Books and study aids other than those listed should be approved by the licensing board or the testing proctor.

Amendments

The licensing board may have amendments to the National Electrical Code®. The board may add or delete sections to the NEC®. A local test may incorporate local amendments. When making application, request a copy of amendments and ask if they are included in the examination.

Private Testing Agencies

The licensing board may make up and administer their own examinations or use a private testing agency. The licensing board reviews tests and sets the criteria for the examination. The private agency administers the test and returns the results to the licensing board.

Special Examinations

The need may arise to have a license as quickly as possible. The local licensing board may permit a special test. At the time of application, request this information, if it is necessary.

Schools/Bookstores

The local licensing board may supply the applicant with a list of public schools, private schools, and bookstores where exam preparation classes are conducted, or where technical material is available for purchase. Ask for this information, if it applies.

Test Preparation

1. Be prepared, mentally ready, and know and understand the basic material that is covered on the test.
2. Only conduct a light review the night before the test.
3. Get a good night's sleep.
4. Eat a light breakfast.
5. Be relaxed, alert, and free of tension.
6. Allow sufficient travel time to get to the test site.
7. Determine the amount of questions per examination section. Calculate the time per question and divide the sections into time zones. This allows you to pace yourself. Generally, questions not answered are marked incorrect.
8. Read each question carefully. Fully understand the question before marking the answer sheet.
9. Time is critical. Too much time spent on any one question could result in questions not answered.
10. Use the Dash Method. When you have used your allotted time for a question, mark a light dash on the answer key alongside the question number. Proceed to the next question. Upon test completion, go back and answer the dashed questions.
11. Generally, if you guess, your first choice is usually right. Do not change your answer unless you are positive you have guessed incorrectly.
12. Tab your NEC® book. Tabs are available through technical bookstores.

ALL FEES ARE NONREFUNDABLE

Pinellas County Construction Licensing Board

11701 BELCHER ROAD, SUITE 102
LARGO, FLORIDA 33773
Telephone 536-4720

JOURNEYMAN APPLICATION FORM

Cert. No. _____   Receipt No. _____   Date: _____

DATE   GRADE

_____   _____
_____   _____
_____   _____
_____   _____

DO NOT FILL IN ABOVE DOUBLE LINE

(Check Appropriate boxes)

Type or Print in ink. Answer all questions.

1. Present Journeyman Certificate No. _____

     From _____ (City)

❶ 2. I am applying for the following:

☐ Plumbing Journeyman   ☐ Air Conditioning Journeyman
☐ Electrical Journeyman   ☐ Pipe Fitting Journeyman
☐ Sheet Metal Journeyman

3. Have you previously applied to this Board for Certification for any type contractor or journeyman? If so, when?

_____

4. Name of Individual to be Certified   Social Security Number

_____

(as you would have it on Certificate)

5. Residence Address _____ City _____ Zip _____
❷ 6. Date of Birth _____ Place of Birth _____
7. Sex: ☐ Male   ☐ Female
8. Telephone: Home _____ Business _____
9. Give names of institutions, locations, length of time spent in each and course:

High School	**Location**	**Years Attended**	**Type of Course**
High School _____	_____	From: 19 _____	
_____	_____	To: 19 _____	_____
Trade School _____	_____	From: 19 _____	
_____	_____	To: 19 _____	_____
Other _____	_____	From: 19 _____	
_____	_____	To: 19 _____	_____

❸

10. Have you previously been employed as any type of licensed journeyman? _____
How long _____ Type journeyman _____
Where _____

Pinellas County Construction Licensing Board

❶ **TYPE OF CERTIFICATE APPLIED FOR**

❷ **PERSONAL INFORMATION**

❸ **SCHOOLS ATTENDED**

continued . . .

Figure 1-4. The journeyman application form provides personal information.

. . . continued from Figure 1-4.

❶
11.   History of employment as a helper, apprentice or journeyman in the profession for which you desire certification; use last six (6) years only.

Name of Firm or Job	Where	When	Duties
_____	_____	_____	_____
_____	_____	_____	_____
_____	_____	_____	_____
_____	_____	_____	_____

❷
12.   Three character **letters** must be submitted from reputable business or professional persons *(not relatives of applicant or present or past employers)* of Pinellas County or the County of applicant's last employment.

13.   If the answer to any of the following questions is "yes" explain fully under "Remarks," giving names, dates, locations, etc.

YES   NO

a.   Have you been convicted of a misdemeanor or felony, or are you presently under a charge of committing a misdemeanor or a felony?   _____ _____

b.   Have you ever been refused a journeyman's or other professional license, or had such a license suspended or revoked?   _____ _____

c.   Are you now doing business, or have you ever done business under a fictitious name? Attach proof of compliance with the Florida Fictitious Name Act.   _____ _____

REMARKS: _____

_____

_____

(Use Additional Sheet If Necessary)

14.   I hereby apply for a Journeyman's Certificate as a _____ Journeyman and enclose the fee in the amount of $50.00. I have read the accompanying instruction sheet and have answered all the questions. I understand that my certificate can be suspended or revoked for good cause shown.

Signed _____
Applicant

❸
State of _____

County of _____

Personally appeared before me, an officer duly authorized to administer an oath,
_____ , of City of
_____ , County of _____ ,
State of _____ , known to me to be the person herein described and subscribing hereto, and on oath deposes and says that the information provided and the statements made in this application are true and correct.

Signature of Applicant _____

Sworn to and subscribed before me this _____ day of _____ 20 _____.

_____
(Notary Public)

My commission expires _____ , 20_____.

Pinellas County Construction Licensing Board

❶   **EMPLOYMENT**

❷   **LETTERS OF REFERENCE**

❸   **SIGNATURE AND NOTARIZATION**

PINELLAS COUNTY CONSTRUCTION LICENSING BOARD
11701 BELCHER ROAD, SUITE 102
LARGO, FL 33773

Information in this box to be filled in by Applicant.
(PRINT OR TYPE)

Applicant _____
(Name of person to be examined)

Address _____
(Same as on application)

Classification _____

CERTIFICATE IN SUPPORT OF JOURNEYMAN APPLICANT'S EXPERIENCE QUALIFICATIONS
(To be attached to application for examination)

The person certifying to his knowledge of the experience of the applicant above named shall complete the form below.
READ THE REVERSE SIDE BEFORE PROCEEDING.

I, _____ , certify that I am personally
Name of Employer *(Print)*

familiar with the work experience of _____
Name of Examinee

during the period from _____ to _____ ❶

and that I know of my own direct knowledge that said applicant was employed as follows:
(Tell in your own words what you know of applicant's experience. Give the dates of employment.
Describe the type of work he performed and his position as worker, apprentice, helper, journeyman,
foreman or supervisory employee. Describe the kind of buildings, structures, projects or equipment
worked upon. (Give any other details that might aid in evaluating his experience.)

_____
_____
_____ ❷
_____
_____

On this _____ day of _____, 20 _____, at _____
I certify under penalty of perjury that the foregoing is true and correct.

Sworn to and subscribed before me this _____

_____   _____   _____
Signature of employer   (License No.) ❸

❹ of _____ , 20 __

(PRINT name of employer)

_____   Address _____
Notary Public   Street

_____
City   State

**WHEN FILED WITH AN APPLICATION THIS CERTIFICATE BECOMES THE PROPERTY
OF THE PCCLB AND IS KEPT AS A MATTER OF RECORD**

RETURN TO APPLICANT

Pinellas County Construction Licensing Board

❶ **DATES OF EMPLOYMENT**

❷ **STATEMENT OF APPLICANT'S EXPERIENCE**

❸ **SIGNATURE OF EMPLOYER**

❹ **NOTARIZATION**

Figure 1-5. The certificate of journeyman applicant's experience qualifications is completed by the employer.

continued . . .

. . . continued from Figure 1-5.

To Persons Requested to Certify to Applicant's Experience:

The applicant named on the reverse side is required to prove his right to take a journeyman's examination by furnishing these certificates in support of his experience shown in his application. Enough certificates are required to prove such experience to the Board. The applicant must have had:

NOT LESS THAN ___* YEARS EXPERIENCE PRECEDING THE FILING OF AN APPLICATION IN THE PARTICULAR CLASSIFICATION OF LICENSE FOR WHICH APPLICATION IS MADE.

❶

He is, therefore, requesting you to certify as to your knowledge of his experience by completing the form on the opposite side.

Certifications must be by former employers <u>licensed as contractors</u>. If former employers are deceased, other licensed contractors familiar with your work experience may verify such experience. **This form must be notarized.**

To be acceptable, the form on the opposite side must be subscribed and the statements therein certified to be true under the penalty of perjury.

<u>Do not mail this form to the Pinellas County Construction Licensing Board.</u>
<u>Return it to the applicant in order that he may attach it to his application.</u>

Your cooperation is earnestly solicited so that the PCCLB can determine whether an applicant has had the experience necessary to become a capable and qualified journeyman.

* **4 years for Electricians**
* **4 years for Plumbers**
* **4 years for Pipe Fitters**
* **4 years for Air Conditioning**
* **3 years for Sheet Metal**

HOW TO COMPUTE YEARS OF EXPERIENCE - USE ANY OF THE FOLLOWING:

❷

1. Completion of a 4-year apprenticeship program equals 4 years; or
2. Completion of 4 years' full-time employment (2,080 hours/year) since leaving (high) school equals 4 years; or
3. Completion of less than 4 years' full-time employment since leaving (high) school can be added to actual part-time hours worked before leaving school once age 16 was attained. This means actual part-time hours worked since 16th birthday and during school years may be added to years of work since leaving school to total 4 years.

The total hours needed to qualify for 4 years equal 8,320 (4 x 2,080). For journeyman classification requiring only 3 years' experience, follow the above rules to total 3 years.

❸

All work <u>must</u> be verified by licensed contractors.

Pinellas County Construction Licensing Board

❶ CERTIFICATION

❷ YEARS OF EXPERIENCE

❸ VERIFICATION

Test Grading

Each licensing board sets the grading standard for examinations. Contact your local licensing board to determine if they provide an examination breakdown and how the test is graded.

Journeyman electrician's examinations may be developed locally by the authority having jurisdiction or may be developed by an independent testing agency. The local licensing board sets standards and approves test questions. They also collect all fees and process all applications.

Test Structure

The local test is written, administered, and graded by the authority having jurisdiction. See Figure 1-6.

The independent test is written and graded by the independent testing agency. See Figure 1-7. It may be administered by the independent testing agency or the authority having jurisdiction.

The journeyman electrician's examination is typically a three hour test with 80 questions. It is a broad-based test containing questions on calculations, trade knowledge, and finding answers to questions in the NEC® code book. When taking the examination, time is critical. All questions not answered are marked wrong. A time frame of three hours provides 2 minutes and 15 seconds for each question (180 min ÷ 80 questions = 2 min 15 sec per question). A kitchen timer or stop watch is ideal for timing.

What to Take to the Examination

1. National Electrical Code® (ANSI/NFPA 70). Generally no notes, examples, or formulas are permitted to be written in the book.
2. Any reference books permitted (e.g., American Electricians' Handbook).
3. A minimum of two lead pencils, or a mechanical pencil with additional lead.
4. A watch or small travel clock.
5. A 6″ flat ruler for sighting lines in tables.
6. A pad of paper.
7. A calculator (with extra batteries or a spare calculator).

Grade Notification

After completing the journeyman electrician's examination, generally the applicant receives a letter with the grade score and license. A common passing grade is 70% for the total examination. See Figure 1-8.

Reciprocity

Jurisdictions may have mutual agreements allowing a journeyman electrician to reciprocate their test scores. This permits the journeyman electrician to perform work in another jurisdiction and not have to repeat the examination. Reciprocity generally requires a higher test score than the minimum passing grade. A test score of 75% is common for reciprocity.

Test Specification Sample

Journeyman Electrician's Exam

Scope
The Journeyman Electrician's Exam tests for competency of the installation, maintenance, modification, planning, and repair of electrical conductors, raceways, and equipment.

Time limit **3 hr**
Questions **80**   **75%** needed to pass exam

THIS EXAM MAY INCLUDE ADDITIONAL NONSCORED TRIAL QUESTIONS

SUBJECT	PERCENT
General Electrical Knowledge	10
Wiring and Protection	25
Wiring Methods and Materials	20
Equipment for General Use	20
Special Occupancies	10
Special Equipment	5
Special Conditions	5
Communications Systems	5

The following references are permitted during the exam:

• *NFPA 70 National Electrical Code®, 2008* Edition
National Fire Protection Association
1 Batterymarch Park
P. O. Box 9101
Quincy, MA 02269-9101, www.nfpa.org

• *Printreading Based on the 2008 National Electrical Code® (NEC®), 2008* Edition
American Technical Publishers, Inc.
1155 W. 175th Street
Homewood, IL 60430, www.go2atp.com

Figure 1-6. An independant testing agency writes and administers the journeyman electrician's examination.

Sample Information Bulletin

Journeyman Electrician's Exam

License Information

The Journeyman Electrician's Exam tests for competency of the installation, maintenance, modification, planning, and repair of electrical conductors, raceways, and equipment.

Exam Outline

80 Questions
3 hr time limit
75% needed to pass exam.

Topic	%
General Electrical Knowledge	10
Wiring and Protection	25
Wiring Methods and Materials	20
Equipment for General Use	20
Special Occupancies	10
Special Equipment	5
Special Conditions	5
Communications Systems	5

The following references are permitted during the exam:

NFPA 70-National Electrical Code®, 2008 Edition
National Fire Protection Association
1 Batterymarch Park
P. O. Box 9101
Quincy, MA 02269-9101, www.nfpa.org

Printreading Based on the 2008 National Electrical Code® (NEC®), 2008 Edition
American Technical Publishers, Inc.
1155 W. 175th Street
Homewood, IL 60430, www.go2atp.com

Figure 1-7. An independent test is written and graded by the independent testing agency.

. . . continued from Figure 1-7.

SAMPLE QUESTIONS

1. A 5 HP 240 V 1ϕ motor drawing 19 A is ___% efficient.
A. 82
B. 89
C. 92
D. 96
Answer: A

2. The ampacity of a #12 Type NM Cu cable used for derating is ___ A.
A. 15
B. 25
C. 30
D. 16
Answer: C

3. Six feet of track lighting in a dwelling shall be computed at ___ VA.
A. 900
B. 0
C. 1080
D. 600
Answer: B

4. The maximum spacing for receptacles in a dwelling is ___′.
A. 6
B. 12
C. 5
D. 10
Answer: B

5. An underground service is called a service ___.
A. drop
B. point
C. lateral
D. cable
Answer: C

6. A ___ is not permitted to be attached to a service riser.
A. telephone line
B. cable TV line
C. computer service
D. all of the above
Answer: D

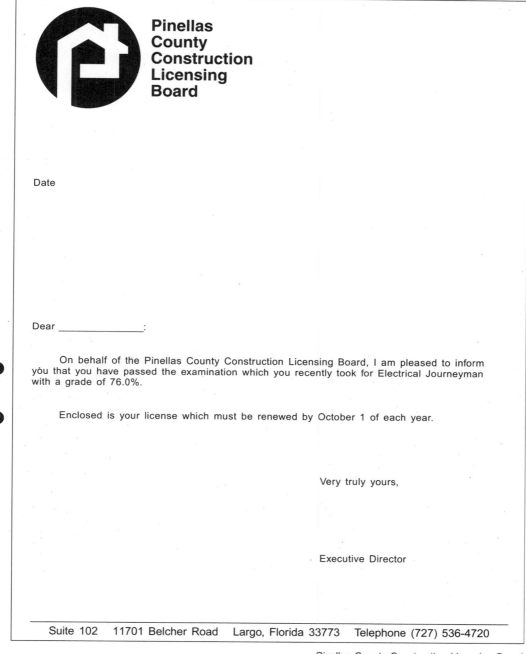

Date

Dear _____:

❶   On behalf of the Pinellas County Construction Licensing Board, I am pleased to inform you that you have passed the examination which you recently took for Electrical Journeyman with a grade of 76.0%.

❷   Enclosed is your license which must be renewed by October 1 of each year.

Very truly yours,

Executive Director

Suite 102   11701 Belcher Road   Largo, Florida 33773   Telephone (727) 536-4720

Pinellas County Construction Licensing Board

❶   **GRADE SCORE**

❷   **LICENSE**

Figure 1-8. A common passing grade is 70% for the journeyman electrician's examination.

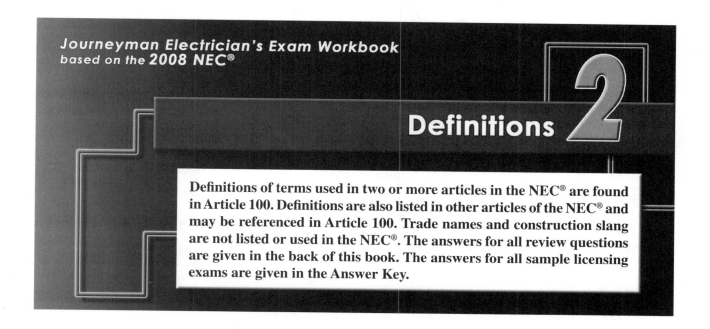

Definitions of terms used in two or more articles in the NEC® are found in Article 100. Definitions are also listed in other articles of the NEC® and may be referenced in Article 100. Trade names and construction slang are not listed or used in the NEC®. The answers for all review questions are given in the back of this book. The answers for all sample licensing exams are given in the Answer Key.

DEFINITIONS

Definitions of terms are found in Article 100. This article is a key for understanding the NEC®. In general, terms used two or more times in the NEC® are listed in Article 100, Definitions. Trade names and construction slang are not listed or used in the NEC®. For example, Romex is a trade name of nonmetallic-sheathed cable. Electricians commonly refer to the ungrounded conductor as either a hot or phase conductor.

Definitions are also listed in other articles of the NEC®. For example, a park trailer is defined in 552.2. A fixed appliance is defined in 550.2. Other definitions are throughout the NEC®.

Accessible: (as pertains to equipment) Admitting close access, not sealed by locked doors, elevated, or other serviceable means. See Figure 2-1.

Example: A disconnect for an A/H in an attic with an access hatch is considered *accessible.*

Ampacity: The current, in amperes, that a wire can carry continuously under the status of use without surpassing its temperature rating.

Example: The *ampacity* of conductors listed in Table 310.16 is based on a set temperature.

Approved: Acceptable to local enforcement.

Example: A lay-in fixture surface-mounted on a drywall ceiling was not *approved* by the inspector.

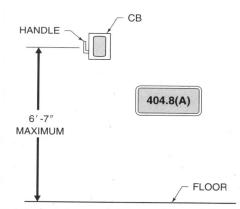

Figure 2-1. Switches and CBs used as switches shall be not more than 6'-7" from the floor.

Attachment Plug (Plug Cap or Cap): An electrical, male connector which is inserted into receptacles. Used with portable cords. Commonly called a cord cap.

Example: An *attachment plug* is NEMA-rated according to voltage and amperage. The two basic types are straight blade and twist lock. NEMA charts are available at local supply houses.

Bonded (Bonding): Connected to establish electrical continuity and conductivity. See Figure 2-2.

Example: The NEC® requires *bonding* of certain equipment to establish electrical continuity and conductivity. Service equipment with metal raceways shall be bonded. Locknuts alone are not acceptable.

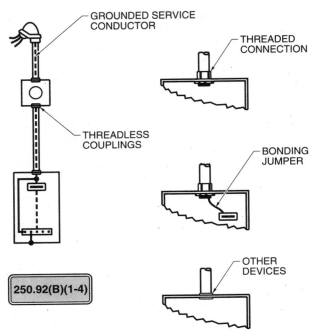

250.92(B)(1-4)

Figure 2-2. Electrical continuity at service equipment is assured by bonding.

Bonding Jumper, Main: The connection of the neutral bar to the service panel, cabinet, or switchboard frame.

Example: The *main bonding jumper* can be a wire, screw, or an acceptable conductor per 250.102(A).

Branch Circuit: The circuit wire between the last overcurrent device protecting the circuit and devices.

Example: Rules and regulations regarding a *branch circuit* are covered in 210.

Building: A structure by itself or one that is separated from connected structures by approved fire walls with all entrances protected by authorized fire doors.

Example: Each house, of a block of row houses with approved fire walls, is considered a *building*.

Continuous Load: A load in which the maximum current is expected to last for three hours or more. See Figure 2-3.

Example: A hot water heater in a dwelling is considered a *continuous load*.

Dwelling Unit: One or more housekeeping rooms for one or more people which contains space for eating, sleeping, and living, with permanent provisions for cooking and sanitation.

Example: A storage building with sleeping quarters does not meet the definition of a *dwelling unit*.

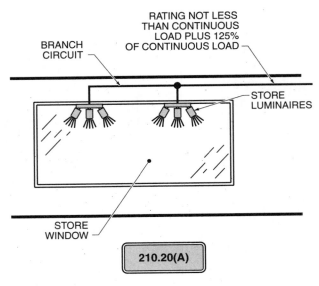

210.20(A)

Figure 2-3. Show window luminaires are considered a continuous load.

Electric Sign: A fixed, stationary, or portable unit containing electric lighting used for advertising and display.

Example: Most AHJs require that an *electric sign* be installed by a licensed sign contractor. The electrician provides wiring to the installation.

Energized: Connected to a voltage source with applied electrical pressure.

Example: The line side of service equipment is *energized*.

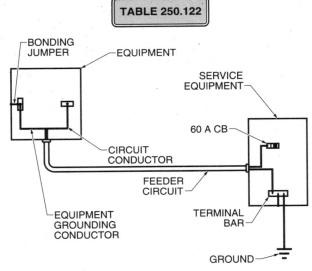

TABLE 250.122

Figure 2-4. The EGC is sized per Table 250.122.

Exposed: (as applied to live parts) Any energized equipment and conductors with which a person might come in contact.

Example: A panel on a construction site used for temporary power has no cover. The wiring and equipment *exposed* presents a hazard.

Feeder: Conductors between service equipment and the last OCPD.

Example: Article 220 is entitled Branch Circuit, *Feeder,* and Service Calcs. Article 215 cover feeders.

Fitting: An electrical accessory such as a locknut or bushing which is used for mechanical instead of electrical functions.

Example: A PVC male adapter is a *fitting.*

Grounded (Grounding): Connected to earth or in direct contact with earth. See Figure 2-5.

Example: Electrodes are *grounded* per 250.52.

Grounded Conductor: A conductor that is connected to earth.

Example: The *grounded conductor* is the neutral conductor per 200.

Grounding Conductor, Equipment: The conductive path installed to connect normally non-current carrying metal parts of equipment together and to the system grounded conductor or to the grounded electrode conductor, or both. See Figure 2-4.

Example: The *equipment grounding conductor* is intended to carry electricity in the event of a fault.

Guarded: A safety barrier, such as a fence, which provides necessary protection for personnel.

Example: A room with a locked door is considered *guarded.*

Hoistway: A vertical opening in which an elevator car operates.

Example: A *hoistway* on a construction site is very dangerous. These openings should be protected by OSHA-approved barricades.

In Sight: Visible within 50′. See Figure 2-6.

Example: A disconnect shall be *in sight* of a motor and driven machinery per 430.102(B).

Interrupting Rating: The maximum current at which a device will interrupt at its rated voltage.

Example: Serious damage could occur if an OCPD is undersized and the fault current exceeds the *interrupting rating.*

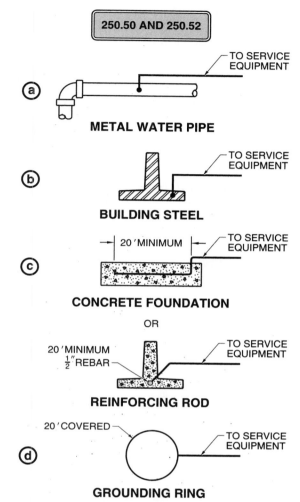

Figure 2-5. Electrical service equipment is grounded per 250.50.

Labeled: Material and equipment so tagged are acceptable to the AHJ and complies with all of the appropriate standards.

Example: Equipment *labeled* UL meets the standards of Underwriters' Laboratories, Inc.

Nonlinear: A load in which the current and voltage do not have the same wave pattern. The voltage and current do not completely work together.

Example: A *nonlinear* load is a load in which the voltage and current are out-of-phase. Generally, the current is lagging.

Overcurrent: Excessive amperage which may cause overheating, short circuit, or ground fault.

Example: Clean connections, the correct wire size, and the correct OCPD size help to avoid *overcurrent.*

Qualified Person: An individual with skills, knowledge, and training of construction and operation of electrical equipment to recognize and avoid electrical hazards.
Example: A licensed journeyman electrician is a *qualified person.*

Raintight: Equipment designed to prevent heavy rain from entering the enclosure.
Example: A disconnect installed out of doors in the open must be *raintight.*

Receptacle Outlet: An electrical female outlet with one or more receptacles.
Example: Hallways at least 10′ or more in length shall have at least one *receptacle outlet* per 210.52(H).

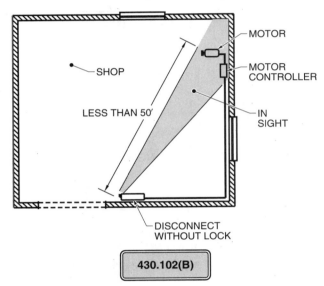

430.102(B)

Figure 2-6. If the disconnect cannot be locked in an open position, it shall be in sight of the motor.

Service Drop: Overhead service wires generally provided by the utility company which attach to the service-entrance conductors on the premises.
Example: Service drop conductors are installed by private utility companies.

Service Lateral: Underground service-entrance conductors.
Example: Most new dwellings are being built with a *service lateral.*

Show Window: Any window that is used for a display or advertising.
Example: A *show window* that is 12′ or longer requires a receptacle above the window.

Special Permission: Written consent of the AHJ.
Example: The AHJ may grant *special permission* per 90.4.

Thermal Protector: (as pertains to motors) A device designed to protect a motor from overheating.
Example: Fractional hp motors generally have a built in *thermal protector.*

Voltage, Nominal: A standard voltage value for circuits and systems.
Example: Nominal voltages include 120, 208, 240, 277, and 480 V.

Watertight: A design that will not permit water to enter the enclosure.
Example: A swimming pool light is required to be watertight.

Name _____ Date _____

Definitions (100)

_____ **1.** Automatic is self-acting, functioning by its own mechanism when actuated by some detached influence, such as ___.
     A. a change in current strength   C. mechanical configuration
     B. temperature   D. either A, B, or C

_____ **2.** An enclosure designed either for surface or flush mounting and provided with a frame, in which a swinging door may be hung is a ___.
     A. cabinet   C. switchboard
     B. panelboard   D. cutout box

_____ **3.** Copper forms a minimum of ___% of the cross-sectional area of a solid copper-clad aluminum wire.
     A. 80   C. 10
     B. 125   D. 12.5

_____ **4.** Ampacity is expressed in ___.
     A. volts × amps   C. volts × watts
     B. amperes   D. mhos

_____ **5.** Intermittent duty is a mode of service that demands operation for alternate intervals of ___.
     A. load and no load   C. load, no load, and rest
     B. load and rest   D. either A, B, or C

_____ **6.** Accessible (as pertains to equipment) means ___.
     A. admitting close approach   C. either A or B
     B. not guarded by locked doors   D. neither A, B, nor C

_____ **7.** ___ is the most common liquid used in transformers.
     A. PCB   C. Askarel
     B. Leactill   D. Tetraetill

_____ **8.** The point of connection between the facilities of the serving utility and the premises wiring is the ___.
     A. transformer tie   C. system connection tie
     B. service tie   D. service point

_____ **9.** A load in which the peak current is assumed to continue for three hours or more is a ___ load.
     A. peak   C. maximum
     B. continuous   D. nominal

_____ 10. An LB is a ___.
  A. conduit body   C. device
  B. fitting   D. service elbow

_____ 11. A ___ is a device which serves to govern, in some predetermined manner, the electric power delivered to the machinery to which it is attached.
  A. switch   C. contactor
  B. relay   D. controller

_____ 12. A space in which an elevator or dumbwaiter operates is a ___.
  A. shaftway   C. well hole
  B. hatchway   D. either A, B, or C

_____ 13. ___ lighting is an arrangement of electrical lighting designed to call attention to certain items, such as the shape of a building.
  A. Festoon   C. Outline
  B. Landscape   D. Flood

_____ 14. Conduit installed underground is considered ___.
  A. in a wet location   C. in a damp location
  B. protected   D. covered

_____ 15. A(n) ___ is a separately derived system.
  A. LV fire alarm   C. smoke detector
  B. transformer   D. elevator motor

_____ 16. A conductor enclosed with a material not considered insulation by the code is ___.
  A. encased   C. sheathed
  B. covered   D. coated

_____ 17. Nominal voltage is ___ voltage.
  A. actual   C. demand
  B. peak   D. assigned system

_____ 18. A steady-state DC circuit has ___.
  A. inductance   C. VARS
  B. capacitance   D. resistance

_____ 19. ___ lighting is a string of outdoor lights suspended between two points.
  A. Festoon   C. Carnival
  B. Outline   D. Pig tail

_____ 20. A(n) ___ is used to convert direct current to alternating current.
  A. dynamo   C. rectifier
  B. static inverter   D. alternator

Name _____ Date _____

Definitions (100)

_____ 1. A(n) ___ switch for use on branch-circuits is rated in amperage and voltage.
  A. general-use snap   C. isolating
  B. motor-circuit   D. general-use

_____ 2. A ___ is an OCPD that opens when an overcurrent passes through it.
  A. thermal cutout   C. fuse
  B. thermal protector   D. neither A, B, nor C

_____ 3. ___ has a locked entry in which machinery may be operated without opening the door to the enclosure.
  A. A cabinet   C. A cutout box
  B. Sealable equipment   D. A safe box

_____ 4. Air ducts are joined in the ___ of an A/C system.
  A. shaftway   C. plenum
  B. hoistway   D. air handler

_____ 5. A car wash is considered a ___ location.
  A. wet   C. dry
  B. damp   D. moist

_____ 6. Equipment which has been tested or meets the proper standards is ___.
  A. labeled   C. listed
  B. certified   D. approved

_____ 7. A disconnect requiring an extension ladder for servicing is considered ___.
  A. isolated   C. unguarded
  B. readily accessible   D. restricted

_____ 8. Equipment installed behind wooden doors which is accessible is considered ___.
  A. exposed   C. covered
  B. concealed   D. isolated

_____ 9. ___ protection is designed to prevent accidental contact with live equipment.
  A. Isolated   C. Concealed
  B. Enclosed   D. Restricted

_____ 10. The ___ is a conductor which connects the neutral of the system to a grounding electrode.
  A. grounded conductor   C. neutral bond
  B. equipment grounding conductor D. grounding conductor

_____ **11.** A voltage of ___ V is not considered a nominal voltage.
        A. 600   C. 208
        B. 277   D. neither A, B, nor C

_____ **12.** A multioutlet assembly is a wiring method designed to hold ___ assembled on the job site.
        A. lighting outlets   C. conductors and receptacles
        B. lighting outlets and receptacles   D. either A or C

_____ **13.** Terms appearing in ___ or more articles are listed in 100.
        A. one   C. three
        B. two   D. four

_____ **14.** A(n) ___ wire is wrapped with a paper type material.
        A. bare   C. insulated
        B. protected   D. covered

_____ **15.** A structure under construction is considered ___.
        A. a damp location   C. a dry location
        B. buried   D. a wet location

_____ **16.** A(n) ___ is an intentional or accidental connection between an electrical circuit and the earth.
        A. ground   C. grounded conductor
        B. grounded   D. effective ground

_____ **17.** ___ is a general term used for materials, fittings, devices, and fixtures for electrical installations.
        A. Supplies   C. Submittals
        B. Equipment   D. Supply house stock

_____ **18.** A ___ circuit is a circuit that energizes signaling equipment.
        A. signaling   C. control
        B. flag   D. low voltage control

_____ **19.** A ___ is a load in which the maximum amperage is expected to continue for three hours or more.
        A. peak load   C. maximum load
         B. continuous load   D. continuous duty load

_____ **20.** Construction designed so that dust will not interfere with its successful operation is ___ construction.
        A. sealed   C. enclosed for dust and fibers
         B. dustproof   D. dustight

Name _____ Date _____

Definitions (100)

_____ 1. ___ is the current in amperes that a wire can carry continuously under the status of use without surpassing its temperature rating.
- A. Fault current
- B. Ampacity
- C. kVA
- D. Nominal current

_____ 2. ___ include(s) fittings, devices, appliances, and fixtures.
- A. Material
- B. Electrical parts
- C. Equipment
- D. Apparatus

_____ 3. A ___ is a type of surface or flush raceway designed to hold wires.
- A. floor duct
- B. multioutlet assembly
- C. cellular metal raceway
- D. busway

_____ 4. A(n) ___ is a service lateral.
- A. equipment mounting system
- B. bus duct
- C. floor duct
- D. neither A, B, nor C

_____ 5. A service lateral is a set of ___ conductors.
- A. drop
- B. aerial
- C. underground
- D. overhead

_____ 6. A piece of equipment is insight from another piece of equipment when not more than ___′ apart.
- A. 50
- B. 75
- C. 100
- D. 25

_____ 7. The ___ is the ratio of the peak demand of the system to the maximum connected load of the system.
- A. nameplate
- B. demand factor
- C. continuous load
- D. connected load

_____ 8. The NEC® recognizes a ___ as a device.
- A. switch
- B. light bulb
- C. pilot light
- D. either A or B

_____ 9. ___ equipment is not readily accessible to persons unless proper means for access are used.
- A. Concealed
- B. Covered
- C. Isolated
- D. Dead front

_____ 10. A luminaire consists of a ___.
- A. housing
- B. ballast
- C. lamp
- D. A, B, or C

Questions 11–20 pertain to definitions in other articles of the NEC®.

_____ **11.** The definition for a *bulk storage plant* is given in ___.
    A. 500.1   C. 503.1
    B. 502.1   D. 515.2

_____ **12.** The definition for a *converter* is given in ___.
    A. 430.2   C. 710.2
    B. 551.2   D. 700.1

_____ **13.** The definition for *laundry area* is given in ___.
    A. 550.2   C. 820.1
    B. 810.4   D. 710.6

_____ **14.** The definition for *critical branch* is given in ___.
    A. 210.3   C. 514.1
    B. 517.2   D. 430.1

_____ **15.** The definition for *feeder assembly* is given in ___.
    A. 550.2   C. 430.2
    B. 215.1   D. 770.1

_____ **16.** The definition for *array* is given in ___.
    A. 690.2   C. 517.3
    B. 520.2   D. 402.1

_____ **17.** The definition for *emergency system* is given in ___.
    A. 400.2   C. 690.1
    B. 517.2   D. 800.1

_____ **18.** The definition for *solar cell* is given in ___.
    A. 690.2   C. 700.1
    B. 517.3   D. 690.1

_____ **19.** The definition for *wire* is given in ___.
    A. 760.1   C. 800.2
    B. 550.1   D. 502.1

_____ **20.** The definition for *hospital* is given in ___.
    A. 502.2   C. 690.1
    B. 550.2   D. 517.2

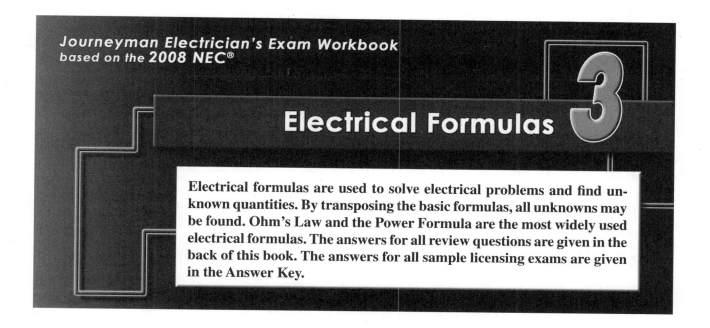
Electrical formulas are used to solve electrical problems and find unknown quantities. By transposing the basic formulas, all unknowns may be found. Ohm's Law and the Power Formula are the most widely used electrical formulas. The answers for all review questions are given in the back of this book. The answers for all sample licensing exams are given in the Answer Key.

OHM'S LAW

Ohm's law is the relationship between the voltage, current, and resistance in an electrical circuit. Ohm's law states that current in a circuit is proportional to the voltage and inversely proportional to the resistance. Any value in these relationships is found using Ohm's law, which is written:

$$I = \frac{E}{R}$$

$$E = R \times I$$

$$R = \frac{E}{I}$$

A commonly used variation of Ohm's law is $I = \frac{V}{R}$. See Figure 3-1.

Current Calculation

Current (I) is the amount of electrons flowing through an electrical circuit. Current is measured in amperes (A). Current may be direct or alternating. *Direct current (DC)* is current that flows in one direction. *Alternating current (AC)* is current that reverses its direction of flow at regular intervals. To calculate current, apply the formula:

$$I = \frac{E}{R}$$
where

I = current (in A)
E = voltage (in V)
R = resistance (in Ω)

also used as $I = \frac{V}{R}$
where

I = current (in A)
V = voltage (in V)
R = resistance (in Ω)

OHM'S LAW AND POWER FORMULA

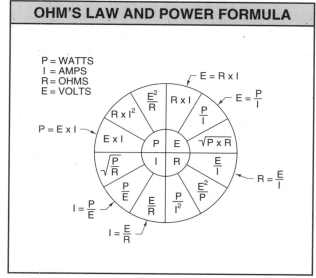

P = WATTS
I = AMPS
R = OHMS
E = VOLTS

Figure 3-1. The values in the inner circle are equal to values in the corresponding outer circle.

Example: Calculating Current

1. An electrical circuit has a resistance of 80 Ω and is connected to a 120 V supply. Calculate the amount of current in the circuit.

$$I = \frac{E}{R}$$

$$I = \frac{120}{80} = 1.5$$

$$I = \textbf{1.5 A}$$

Voltage Calculation

Voltage (E) is the amount of electrical pressure in a circuit. Voltage is measured in volts (V). Voltage is produced by the conversion of chemical energy (battery), light (photocell), electromagnetic energy (generator), heat (thermocouple), pressure (piezo electricity), or friction (static electricity) to electrical energy. Voltage is produced by generating an excess of electrons at one terminal of a voltage source and a deficiency of electrons at the other terminal. The greater the difference in electrons between the terminals, the higher the voltage. To calculate voltage, apply the formula:

$$E = I \times R$$
where
E = voltage (in V)
I = current (in A)
R = resistance (in Ω)

Example: Calculating Voltage

2. An electrical circuit has 5 A of current and a resistance of 46 Ω. Calculate the voltage in the circuit.

$$E = I \times R$$
$$E = 5 \times 46 = 230$$
$$E = \textbf{230 V}$$

Resistance Calculation

Resistance (R) is opposition to the flow of electrons. Resistance is measured in ohms (Ω). *Conductors* are materials through which current flows easily. Examples of conductors include copper, aluminum, brass, gold, and other metals. *Insulators* are materials through which current cannot flow easily. Examples of insulators include rubber, glass, plastic, paper, varnish, and dry wood. To calculate resistance, apply the formula:

$$R = \frac{E}{I}$$
where
R = resistance (in Ω)
E = voltage (in V)
I = current (in A)

Example: Calculating Resistance

3. An electrical circuit draws 8 A when connected to a 460 V supply. Calculate the resistance of the circuit.

$$R = \frac{E}{I}$$

$$R = \frac{460}{8} = 57.5$$

$$R = \textbf{57.5 Ω}$$

POWER FORMULA

The power formula is the relationship between the voltage, current, and power in an electrical circuit. The power formula states that the power in a circuit is equal to the voltage times the current. Any value in these relationships is found using the power formula, which is written:

$$P = E \times I \times PF$$
$$E = \frac{P}{I \times PF}$$
$$I = \frac{P}{E \times PF}$$
Note: PF = power factor

Power Calculation

Power is the rate of doing work or using energy. Power may be expressed as true or apparent. *True power* is the actual power used in an electrical circuit. True power is measured using a wattmeter and is expressed in watts (W). *Apparent power* is the product of voltage and current in a circuit calculated without considering the phase shift that may be present between total voltage and current in the circuit. Apparent power is measured in volt-amperes (VA). A phase shift exists in most AC circuits that contain devices causing capacitance or inductance.

Capacitance is the property of an electrical device that permits the storage of electrically separated charges when potential differences exist between the conductors. *Inductance* is the property of a circuit that causes it to oppose a change in current due to energy stored in a magnetic field. All coils (motor windings, transformers, solenoids, etc.) create inductance in an electrical circuit. True power equals apparent power in an electrical circuit containing only resistance. True power is less than apparent power in a circuit containing inductance or capacitance. To calculate apparent power, apply the formula:

$$P_A = E \times I$$
where
P_A = apparent power (in VA)
E = measured voltage (in V)
I = measured current (in A)

Example: Calculating Apparent Power

4. An electrical circuit has a measured current of 25 A and a measured voltage of 440 V. Calculate the apparent power of the circuit.

$$P_A = E \times I$$
$$P_A = 440 \times 25 = 11{,}000$$
$$P_A = \textbf{11{,}000 VA}$$

To calculate true power, apply the formula:
$$P_T = I^2 \times R$$
where
P_T = true power (in W)
I = current (in A)
R = resistance (in Ω)

Example: Calculating True Power

5. An electrical circuit has a current of 25 A and a total resistive component of 14.75 Ω. Calculate the true power of the circuit.

$$P_T = I^2 \times R$$
$$P_T = (25)^2 \times 14.75$$
$$P_T = 625 \times 14.75 = 9218.75$$
$$P_T = \textbf{9219 W}$$

Power factor (PF) is the ratio of true power used in an AC circuit to apparent power delivered to the circuit. Power factor is expressed as a percentage. True power equals apparent power when the power factor is 100%. When the power factor is less than 100%, the circuit is less efficient and has higher operating costs. To calculate power factor, apply the formula:

$$PF = \frac{P_T}{P_A}$$
where

PF = power factor (in %)
P_T = true power (in W)
P_A = apparent power (in VA)

Examples: Calculating Power Factor

6. The apparent power of an electrical circuit is 11,000 VA and the true power is 9219 W. Calculate the power factor of the circuit.

$$PF = \frac{P_T}{P_A}$$
$$PF = \frac{9219}{11{,}000} \times 100 = 83.8$$
$$PF = \textbf{83.8\%}$$

7. A 120 V appliance is rated at 1200 W. What is the current?

$$I = \frac{P}{E}$$
$$I = \frac{1200}{120} = 10$$
$$I = \textbf{10 A}$$

8. A 120 V appliance is rated at 1200 W. What is the resistance?

$$R = \frac{E^2}{P}$$
$$R = \frac{120 \times 120}{1200} = 12$$
$$R = \textbf{12 Ω}$$

9. An appliance draws 10 A and has a resistance of 12 Ω. What is the wattage?

$$P = I^2 \times R$$
$$P = 10 \times 10 \times 12 = 1200$$
$$P = \textbf{1200 W}$$

10. A 120 V appliance has 12 Ω of resistance. What is the wattage?

$$P = \frac{E^2}{R}$$
$$P = \frac{120 \times 120}{12} = 1200$$
$$P = \textbf{1200 W}$$

11. An appliance is rated at 1200 W and has a current of 10 A. What is the resistance?

$$R = \frac{P}{I^2}$$

$$R = \frac{1200}{10 \times 10} = 12$$

$$R = \mathbf{12\ \Omega}$$

SERIES CIRCUIT

A *series circuit* is a circuit with only one path for current to flow. The flow must be continuous. In a series-connected circuit with three light bulbs, an open or blown light bulb causes all lamps to cease operating. See Figure 3-2.

E_T – In a series circuit, the sum of all the voltage drops equal the total voltage applied.

$$E_T = E_1 + E_2 + E_3$$

I_T – In a series circuit, the current is the same in all parts of the circuit.

$$I_T = I_1 = I_2 = I_3$$

R_T – In a series circuit, the sum of all the resistances equal the total resistance.

$$R_T = R_1 + R_2 + R_3$$

TOTAL RESISTANCE – SERIES CIRCUIT

A series circuit has resistances of 500 Ω, 700 Ω, and 100 Ω. Calculate the total resistance in the circuit.

$$R_T = R_1 + R_2 + R_3$$
$$R_T = 500 + 700 + 100 = 1300$$
$$R_T = \mathbf{1300\ \Omega}$$

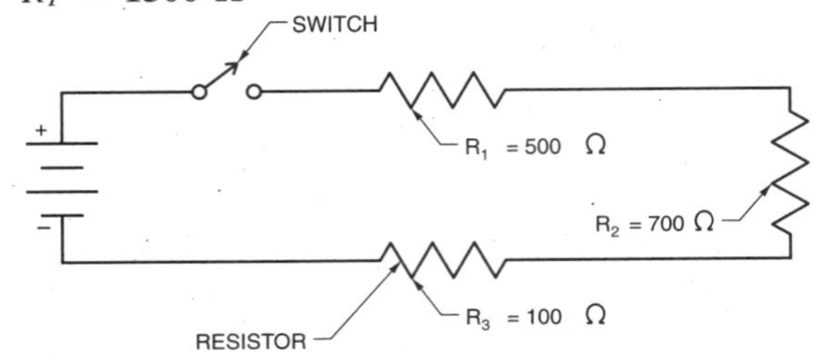

Figure 3-2. A series circuit has only one path for current to flow.

Examples: Series Circuit

A series circuit contains a 5 Ω (R_1), 10 Ω (R_2), and 15 Ω (R_3) resistor connected to a 120 V supply.

12. What is the total resistance?

$$R_T = R_1 + R_2 + R_3$$
$$R_T = 5 + 10 + 15 = 30$$
$$R_T = \mathbf{30\ \Omega}$$

13. What is the total current?

$$I_T = \frac{E_t}{R_t}$$

$$I_T = \frac{120}{30} = 4$$

$$I_T = \mathbf{4\ A}$$

14. What is the voltage drop?

$$E_1 = I_1 \times R_1$$
$$E_1 = 4 \times 5 = 20$$
$$E_1 = \mathbf{20\ V}$$

$$E_2 = I_2 \times R_2$$
$$E_2 = 4 \times 10 = 40$$
$$E_2 = \mathbf{40\ V}$$

$$E_3 = I_3 \times R_3$$
$$E_3 = 4 \times 15 = 60$$
$$E_3 = \mathbf{60\ V}$$

$$E_T = E_1 + E_2 + E_3$$
$$E_T = 20 + 40 + 60 = 120$$
$$E_T = \mathbf{120\ V}$$

PARALLEL CIRCUITS

The majority of circuits are wired in parallel. Unlike the series-connected circuit, when three light bulbs are connected in parallel and one light bulb blows or opens, the other two will still operate. A *parallel circuit* is a circuit with two or more paths for current to flow. See Figure 3-3.

E_T – Voltage is equal in all branches.

$$E_T = E_1 = E_2 = E_3$$

I_T – In a parallel circuit, the amperage divides according to each parallel resistance. The total current is the sum of all the amperages.

$$I_T = I_1 + I_2 + I_3$$

R_T – In a parallel circuit, the reciprocal of the total resistance equals the sum of the reciprocals of the resistances in each branch. As the resistance of the parallel branches increase, the total resistance decreases. The total resistance in a parallel branch is always less than the smallest resistance. A *reciprocal* is the inverse relationship of two numbers. For example, to find the reciprocal of 6, divide 1 by 6. The reciprocal of 6 is ⅙.

TOTAL RESISTANCE – PARALLEL CIRCUIT

A parallel circuit has resistances of $2\,\Omega$ and $4\,\Omega$. Calculate the total resistance in the circuit.

$$R_T = \frac{R_1 \times R_2}{R_1 + R_2}$$

$$R_T = \frac{2 \times 4}{2 + 4} = \frac{8}{6} = 1.33$$

$$R_T = \mathbf{1.33\ \Omega}$$

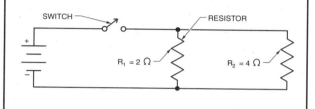

Figure 3-3. A parallel circuit has two or more paths for current to flow.

To calculate equal resistors connected in parallel, apply the formula:

$$R_T = \frac{R_1}{N}$$

N = Number of resistors

To calculate two resistors connected in parallel, apply the formula:

$$R_T = \frac{R_1 \times R_2}{R_1 + R_2}$$

To calculate three or more resistors connected in parallel, apply the formula:

$$R_T = \frac{1}{\dfrac{1}{R_1} + \dfrac{1}{R_2} + \dfrac{1}{R_3}}$$

Examples: Parallel Circuits

A circuit contains a $6\,\Omega$ (R_1), $8\,\Omega$ (R_2), and $12\,\Omega$ (R_3) resistor connected in parallel across a 120 V power source.

15. What is E_T?

$$E_T = E_1 = E_2 = E_3$$

$$E_T = \mathbf{120\ V}$$

16. What is R_T?

$$R_T = \frac{1}{\dfrac{1}{R_1} + \dfrac{1}{R_2} + \dfrac{1}{R_3}}$$

$$R_T = \frac{1}{\dfrac{1}{6} + \dfrac{1}{8} + \dfrac{1}{12}}$$

$$R_T = \frac{1}{.166 + .125 + .083}$$

$$R_T = \frac{1}{.374} = 2.67$$

$$R_T = \mathbf{2.67\ \Omega}$$

17. What is I_T?

$$I_T = \frac{E_T}{R_T}$$

$$I_T = \frac{120}{2.67} = 44.9$$

$$I_T = \mathbf{45\ A}$$

18. What is I_1, I_2, and I_3?

$$I_1 = \frac{E_1}{R_1}$$

$$I_1 = \frac{120}{6} = 20$$

$$I_1 = \mathbf{20\ A}$$

$$I_2 = \frac{E_2}{R_2}$$

$$I_2 = \frac{120}{8} = 15$$

$$I_2 = \mathbf{15\ A}$$

$$I_3 = \frac{E_3}{R_3}$$

$$I_3 = \frac{120}{12} = 10$$

$$I_3 = \mathbf{10\ A}$$

SERIES/PARALLEL CIRCUITS

Series/parallel circuits are combinations of series and parallel circuits. To solve for total resistance, the formulas for series and parallel circuits must be applied. The parallel branches must be reduced to an equivalent resistance (R_Q), which is the total resistance for a parallel branch. Reducing a parallel branch to an equivalent resistance value does not change the total resistance of the circuit.

Examples: Series/Parallel Circuits

19. A 5 Ω resistor is connected in series with 6 Ω and 10 Ω resistors connected in parallel. What is the total resistance of the circuit?

1. Solve for parallel branch equivalent resistance.

$$R_Q = \frac{R_1 \times R_2}{R_1 + R_2}$$

$$R_Q = \frac{6 \times 10}{6 + 10}$$

$$R_Q = \frac{60}{16}$$

$$R_Q = 3.75 \ \Omega$$

2. Substitute R_Q for the parallel branch and solve as a series circuit.

$$R_T = R_1 + R_Q$$
$$R_T = 5 + 3.75$$
$$R_T = \mathbf{8.75 \ \Omega}$$

20. A circuit has a 4 Ω resistor connected in series with four 4 Ω resistors connected in parallel. What is the total circuit resistance?

1. Solve for parallel branch equivalent resistance.

$$R_Q = \frac{R_1}{N}$$

$$R_Q = \frac{4}{4}$$

$$R_{Qs} = 1 \ \Omega$$

2. Substitute R_Q for the parallel branch and solve as a series circuit.

$$R_T = R_1 + R_Q$$
$$R_T = 4 + 1$$
$$R_T = \mathbf{5 \ \Omega}$$

21. A circuit has a 2 Ω resistor connected in series with a 4 Ω, 6 Ω, and an 8 Ω resistor connected in parallel. What is the total circuit resistance?

1. Solve for parallel branch equivalent resistance.

$$R_Q = \frac{1}{\dfrac{1}{R_1} + \dfrac{1}{R_2} + \dfrac{1}{R_3}}$$

$$R_Q = \frac{1}{\dfrac{1}{4} + \dfrac{1}{6} + \dfrac{1}{8}}$$

$$R_Q = \frac{1}{.25 + .167 + .125}$$

$$R_Q = \frac{1}{.542}$$

$$R_Q = 1.84 \ \Omega$$

2. Substitute R_Q for the parallel branch and solve as a series circuit.

$$R_T = R_1 + R_Q$$
$$R_T = 2 + 1.84$$
$$R_T = \mathbf{3.84 \ \Omega}$$

HORSEPOWER

Electrical power is the calculation of the amount of work for a set time period. One electrical horsepower equals 746 W. The ft-lb is a measurement of mechanical power per second or minute. The horsepower is also another method to measure mechanical power. One HP equals 33,000 ft-lb per minute. This is the basis for the relationship between mechanical and electrical energy. See Figure 3-4.

Electrical horsepower is found by applying the formula:

$$HP = \frac{I \times E \times E_{ff}}{746}$$

where
HP = horsepower
I = current (in A)
E = voltage (in V)
E_{ff} = efficiency (in %)
746 = constant

Any value in a formula may be found by transposing the values. For example, to find the FLC of a motor (which is measured in A), apply the formula:

$$I = \frac{HP \times 746}{E \times E_{ff}}$$

Examples: Horsepower

22. A 20 A, 240 V, 1ϕ motor has an 85% efficiency rating. What is the HP?

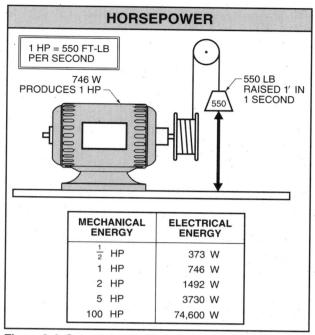

HORSEPOWER

1 HP = 550 FT-LB PER SECOND

746 W PRODUCES 1 HP

550 LB RAISED 1' IN 1 SECOND

MECHANICAL ENERGY	ELECTRICAL ENERGY
$\frac{1}{2}$ HP	373 W
1 HP	746 W
2 HP	1492 W
5 HP	3730 W
100 HP	74,600 W

Figure 3-4. One mechanical horsepower equals 33,000 ft-lb per minute (550 ft-lb per second). One electrical horsepower equals 746 W.

$$HP = \frac{I \times E \times E_{ff}}{746}$$

$$HP = \frac{20 \times 240 \times .85}{746} = 5.5$$

$$HP = \textbf{5.5 HP}$$

23. A 12 A, 240 V, 1ϕ motor has a 77% efficiency rating. What is the HP?

$$HP = \frac{I \times E \times E_{ff}}{746}$$

$$HP = \frac{12 \times 20 \times .77}{746} = 2.9$$

$$HP = \textbf{2.9 HP}$$

24. What is the FLC of a 5 HP, 230 V motor with a 73% efficiency rating?

$$I = \frac{HP \times 746}{E \times E_{ff}}$$

$$I = \frac{5 \times 746}{230 \times .73} = 22.2$$

$$I = \textbf{22 A}$$

25. What is the FLC of a 3 HP, 230 V motor with a 60% efficiency rating?

$$I = \frac{HP \times 746}{E \times E_{ff}}$$

$$I = \frac{3 \times 746}{230 \times .60} = 16.2$$

$$I = \textbf{16 A}$$

EFFICIENCY (MOTORS 1ϕ)

All electrical equipment has losses from heat and friction. *Losses* is the difference between a motor's input and output. For example, a motor with a 1840 W input and a 746 W output has losses of 1094 W. *Efficiency* is the output divided by the input of a motor. For example, a 16 A, 1 HP, 115 V, 1ϕ motor may have an efficiency rating of 40%. Efficiency is found by applying the formula:

$$E_{ff} = \frac{HP \times 746}{I \times E}$$

where

E_{ff} = efficiency (in %)
HP = horsepower
746 = constant
I = current (in A)
E = voltage (in V)

Efficiency is also found by applying the formula:

$$E_{ff} = \frac{Output}{Input}$$

where

E_{ff} = efficiency (in %)
$Output = HP \times 746$ (in W)
$Input = V \times A$ (in W)

Variations of this formula are:

$$Input = \frac{Output}{E_{ff}}$$

$$Output = Input \times E_{ff}$$

Examples: Efficiency

26. What is the efficiency of a 13.2 A, 2 HP, 208 V, 1ϕ motor?

$$E_{ff} = \frac{HP \times 746}{I \times E}$$

$$E_{ff} = \frac{2 \times 746}{13.2 \times 208} = .54$$

$$E_{ff} = \textbf{54\%}$$

27. A 2 HP, 240 V, 1ϕ motor draws 8 A. What is the efficiency?

$$E_{ff} = \frac{Output}{Input}$$

$$E_{ff} = \frac{HP \times 746}{V \times A}$$

$$E_{ff} = \frac{2 \times 746}{240 \times 8}$$

$$E_{ff} = \frac{1492}{1920} = .777$$

$$E_{ff} = \textbf{77.7\%}$$

28. A 2 HP, 240 V, 1ϕ motor draws 8 A and is 77.7% efficient. What is the input?

$$Input = \frac{Output}{E_{ff}}$$

$$Input = \frac{1492}{.777} = 1920$$

$$Input = \textbf{1920 W}$$

29. A 2 HP, 240 V, 1ϕ motor draws 8 A and is 77.7% efficient. What is the output?

$Output = Input \times E_{ff}$
$Output = 1920 \times .777 = 1492$
$Output = \textbf{1492 W}$

30. A 2 HP, 240 V, 1ϕ motor draws 8 A. What are the losses?

$Losses = Input - Output$
$Losses = 1920 - 1492 = 428$
$Losses = \textbf{428 W}$

TRANSFORMERS (1ϕ)

Transformers operate on the principle of mutual induction. *Mutual induction* is voltage caused in one circuit by a change in current by another circuit. Transformers have a primary winding and a secondary winding. Transformers transfer energy from the primary winding to the secondary winding. Transformers can change the voltage and current, but there is no change of power. The primary winding's power input equals the secondary winding's power output when the transformer is 100% efficient. Transformers are generally considered 100% efficient. Transformers are rated in kVA (kilovolt amps). The k in kVA stands for 1000. When working transformer problems,

kVA is often expressed as VA. For example, a 5 kVA transformer is a 5000 VA transformer.

Transformers are very efficient. They are considered 98.2% efficient. In general, for calculation purposes, transformers are considered 100%. In a 100% efficient transformer, the primary kVA equals the secondary kVA, and losses are disregarded.

Transformers of 600 V or less shall have overcurrent protection per Table 450.3(B). A transformer having a primary current of 9 A or more with an OCPD on the primary rated or set at not more than 125%, does not require an OCPD for the secondary. Where the 125% current rating does correspond to a standard size device, the next higher standard rating shall be permitted per Table 450.3(B), Note 1. See 240.6.

The current of a transformer's primary is found by applying the formula:

$$I_P = \frac{kVA \times 1000}{E_P}$$

where
I_P = current of primary (in A)
kVA = kilovolt amps
E_P = voltage of primary (in V)

The current of a transformer's secondary is found by applying the formula:

$$I_S = \frac{kVA \times 1000}{E_S}$$

The kVA of a transformer is found by applying the formula:

$$kVA = \frac{I_S \times E_S}{1000}$$

Examples: Transformers

31. A 5 kVA, 1ϕ, step-up transformer transforms 120 V to 240 V. What is the primary and secondary current? (Efficiency is 100%.)
Primary

$$I_p = \frac{kVA \times 1000}{E_P}$$

$$I_p = \frac{5 \times 1000}{120}$$

$$I_p = \frac{5000}{120} = 41.6$$

$$I_p = \textbf{41.6 A}$$

Secondary

$$I_S = \frac{kVA \times 1000}{E_S}$$

$$I_S = \frac{5 \times 1000}{240}$$

$$I_S = \frac{5000}{240} = 20.8$$

$$I_S = \mathbf{20.8\ A}$$

32. The secondary voltage of a 1ϕ transformer is 240 V. The current is 12.5 A. What is the primary kVA? (Efficiency is 100%.)

$$kVA = \frac{I_S \times E_S}{1000}$$

$$kVA = \frac{12.5 \times 240}{1000}$$

$$kVA = \frac{3000}{1000} = 3$$

$$kVA = \mathbf{3\ kVA}$$

33. A 10 kVA, 1ϕ step-down transformer (240 V to 120 V) is needed to supply a subpanel. What size CB is required for primary protection? (Efficiency is 100%.)

$$I_P = \frac{kVA \times 1000}{E_P}$$

$$I_P = \frac{10 \times 1000}{240}$$

$$I_P = \frac{10,000}{240} = 41.6$$

$$I_P = \mathbf{42\ A}$$

Table 450.3(B): 42 A × 125% = 52.5 A
240.6: *CB* = **60 A**

34. A 10 kVA, 1ϕ step-down transformer (240 V to 120 V) is needed to supply a sub-panel. The secondary overcurrent protection is set at 125% of the secondary FLC. What is the maximum size CB required for primary protection? (Efficiency is 100%.)
Table 450.3(B): 42 A × 250% = 105 A
240.6: *CB* = **100 A**

Transformer Efficiency

Transformers are very efficient in the range of 85% to 99%. The efficiency increases with the kVA rating of the transformer. Generally, transformers are calculated at 100%. Copper, hysteresis, and eddy currents are types of losses in transformers. To compensate for copper loss, the size of the conductors are increased.

Hysteresis is a lagging in values resulting in a changing magnetization in a magnetic material. To compensate for hysteresis, transformer manufacturers have replaced iron as the core material with laminated, silicon steel.

An *eddy current* is an unwanted, induced current in the core of a transformer. To compensate for eddy currents, manufacturers insulated the laminated sections of the transformer core.

Examples: Transformer Efficiency

35. A 2 kVA, 120/240 V, 1ϕ transformer is 93% efficient. What is the primary power?

$$Input = \frac{Output}{E_{ff}}$$

$$Input = \frac{2000}{93} = 2150$$

$$Input = \mathbf{2150\ W}$$

36. What is the primary and secondary current?
Primary

$$I_P = \frac{P}{E}$$

$$I_P = \frac{2150}{120} = 17.9$$

$$I_P = \mathbf{17.9\ A}$$

Secondary

$$I_S = \frac{P}{E}$$

$$I_S = \frac{2000}{240} = 8.33$$

$$I_S = \mathbf{8.33\ A}$$

37. How much power is lost due to transformer losses?
Losses = Input – Output
Losses = 2150 – 2000 = 150
Losses = **150 W**

Ratio

A *ratio* is the whole numbers designating relationship between high voltage and low voltage. For example, a transformer with a 120 V primary and a 480 V secondary has a ratio of 1 to 4 (expressed as 1:4).

$$R = \frac{P}{S}$$

where
R = ratio
P = primary
S = secondary

Example: Ratio

38. A transformer has a 120 V primary and a 12 V secondary. What is the ratio?

$$R = \frac{P}{S}$$

$$R = \frac{120}{12} = 10$$

$$R = \mathbf{10 : 1}$$

TEMPERATURE CONVERSION

Temperature is a measurement of the intensity of heat. *Ambient temperature* is the temperature of the air surrounding a device. Current flowing in a conductor produces heat. The heat produced in an electrical circuit may be by design, such as from a heating element, or unintentional, as from a bad conductor splice. Unintentional heat deteriorates insulation and lubrication, and can destroy electric devices.

Temperature rise is an increase in temperature above ambient temperature. All electric and electronic devices produce heat and are designed to function correctly within a given temperature rise. Temperature is usually measured in degrees Fahrenheit (°F) or degrees Celsius (°C). See Figure 3-5.

Converting Fahrenheit to Celsius

To convert a Fahrenheit temperature reading to Celsius, subtract 32 from the Fahrenheit reading and divide by 1.8. To convert Fahrenheit to Celsius, apply the formula:

$$°C = \frac{°F - 32}{1.8}$$

where

°C = degrees Celsius
°F = degrees Fahrenheit
32 = difference between bases
1.8 = ratio between bases

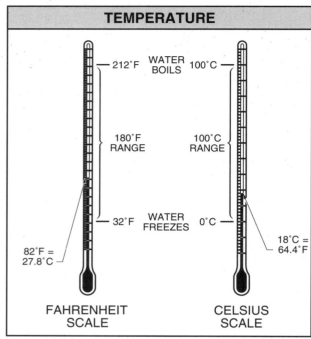

Figure 3-5. Temperature is usually measured in degrees Fahrenheit (°F) or degrees Celsius (°C).

Example: Converting Fahrenheit to Celsius

39. A digital thermometer indicates a reading of 185°F. Convert the Fahrenheit temperature to Celsius.

$$°C = \frac{°F - 32}{1.8}$$

$$°C = \frac{185 - 32}{1.8}$$

$$°C = \frac{153}{1.8} = 85$$

$$°C = \mathbf{85°C}$$

Converting Celsius to Fahrenheit

To convert a Celsius temperature reading to Fahrenheit, multiply 1.8 by the Celsius reading and add 32. To convert Celsius to Fahrenheit, apply the formula:

$$°F = (1.8 \times °C) + 32$$

where

°F = degrees Fahrenheit

1.8 = ratio between bases

°C = degrees Celsius

32 = difference between bases

Example: Converting Celsius to Fahrenheit

40. A temperature monitor indicates 55°C. Convert the Celsius temperature to Fahrenheit.

$°F = (1.8 \times °C) + 32$

$°F = (1.8 \times 55) + 32$

$°F = 99 + 32 = 131$

$°F = \mathbf{131°F}$

BUSBAR CALCULATIONS

Busbars are commonly used in switchboards, load centers, and panelboards. Busbars are generally uninsulated. The constant amperage for a bare copper (Cu) busbar is not permitted to exceed 1000 A/sq in. of the cross-sectional area of the bar. For aluminum (Al) busbars, the constant amperage is not permitted to exceed 700 A/sq in. of the cross-sectional area of the bar per 366.23(A). To calculate the ampacity of a busbar, apply the following formula:

busbar ampacity = *t* × *w* × constant

where

busbar ampacity = ampacity of busbar (in A)

t = thickness (in in.)

w = width (in in.)

constant = 1000 for Cu and 700 for AL

Examples: Calculating Busbar Ampacity

41. What is the ampacity of a ¼″ thick by 3″ wide Cu busbar?

busbar ampacity = *t* × *w* × constant

busbar ampacity = .25 × 3 × 1000

busbar ampacity = .75 × 1000

busbar ampacity = **750 A**

42. What is the ampacity of a ½″ thick by 2″ wide Al busbar?

busbar ampacity = *t* × *w* × constant

busbar ampacity = .50 × 2 × 700

busbar ampacity = 1 × 700

busbar ampacity = **700 A**

VOLTAGE DROP

The NEC® recommends that a voltage drop not exceed 3% of the source voltage for branch circuits per 210.19(A)(1), FPN 4. The NEC® recommends that a voltage drop not exceed 3% of the source voltage for feeders per 215.2(A)(3), FPN 2. The NEC® recommends that a voltage drop not exceed 5% of the source voltage for a combination of feeders and branch circuits per 215.2(A)(3), FPN 2.

The *K factor* is the resistivity of a conductor based on one mil-foot of wire at a set temperature. K is based on the properties of conductors per Ch 9, Table 8. For example, an uncoated 1000 kcmil Cu conductor at 75°C has a resistance of 0.0129 ohms/kFT. To find the resistance for 1′ of this conductor, move the decimal point in 0.0129 (constant/1000′) three places to left. The resistance of 1′ of this conductor is 12.9 μΩ (constant/1′).

Two methods are used to find K; one for approximate K and one for exact K. The approximate K factor is most commonly used. Either K may be used in the voltage drop formula.

Approximate K may be found by using Ch 9, Table 8. To find approximate K for any 1ɸ conductor, always double the constant. To find approximate K for any 3ɸ conductor, multiply the constant by 1.73, which is the $\sqrt{3}$.

The approximate K for 1ɸ Cu is 25.8 μΩ (12.9 μΩ × 2 = 25.8 μΩ). The approximate K for 1ɸ Al is 42.4 μΩ (21.2 μΩ × 2 = 42.4 μΩ). The approximate K for 3ɸ Cu is 22.3 μΩ (12.9 μΩ × 1.73 = 22.3 μΩ). The approximate K for 3ɸ Al is 36.6 μΩ (21.2 μΩ × 1.73 = 36.6 μΩ).

To apply the voltage drop formula, K must be known. To find exact K, apply the formula:

$$K = \frac{R \times CM}{1000}$$

where

K = resistivity of a conductor at a set temperature (in Ω)

R = resistance of conductors (per Ch 9, Table 8)

CM = circular mils (in area)

1000 = constant

Voltage drop is the voltage that is lost due to the resistance of conductors. The longer the conductor, for a given size, the larger the loss. To compensate for voltage drop, a larger conductor is selected, or the voltage may be increased (if available). Voltage drop may be expressed as a percent. To find the percent of voltage drop, apply the formula:

$$VD = \frac{Line\ Loss}{Supply\ Voltage} \times 100$$

where

VD = voltage drop (in %)

Line Loss = loss of volts

Supply Voltage = source voltage

100 = constant (to obtain %)

Voltage drop is found by applying the formula:

$$VD = \frac{K \times I \times D}{CM}$$

where

VD = voltage drop (in V)

K = resistivity of a conductor at a set temperature (in Ω) (Use approximate K.)

I = current (in A)

D = distance (one way) (in feet)

CM = circular mils (in area)

K factor is based on the properties of conductors per Ch 9, Table 8.

Examples: Voltage Drop

43. What is the recommended voltage drop for a 120 V, 208 V, and 240 V branch circuit?

210.19(A)(1), FPN 4:

120 V × 3% = **3.6 V**

208 V × 3% = **6.24 V**

240 V × 3% = **7.2 V**

44. What is the exact K for #10 solid Cu conductor in a 1φ system?

Ch 9, Table 8: R = 1.21 Ω

Ch 9, Table 8: CM = 10,380

$$K = \frac{R \times CM}{1000}$$

$$K = \frac{1.21 \times 10,380}{1000}$$

$$K = 12.56 \times 2 \ (for\ 1\phi) = 25.12$$

$$K = \textbf{25.12}\,\Omega$$

45. A 15 A, 120 V, 1φ circuit has a wire run of 150′. What size Cu wire is required? (Use approximate K.)

Ch 9, Table 8: 1φ Cu = 25.8 Ω

210.19(A)(1), FPN 4: 120 V × 3% = 3.6 V

$$CM = \frac{K \times I \times D}{VD}$$

$$CM = \frac{25.8 \times 15 \times 150}{3.6}$$

$$CM = \frac{58,050}{3.6} = 16,125$$

Ch 9, Table 8: #8 kcmil = 16,510 CM

*Cu wire = **#8 kcmil***

46. A 15 A, 120 V, 1φ branch circuit has a wire run of 150′. What is the VD with solid #10 Cu wire? (Use approximate K.)

K for 1φ Cu = 25.8 Ω

Ch 9, Table 8: #10 Cu = 10,380 CM

$$VD = \frac{K \times I \times D}{CM}$$

$$VD = \frac{25.8 \times 15 \times 150}{10,380}$$

$$VD = \frac{58,050}{10,380} = 5.59$$

$$VD = \textbf{5.59 V}$$

47. A 15 A, 120 V, 1φ branch circuit has a wire run of 150′. What is the percentage of VD with solid #10 Cu wire? (Use approximate K.)

$$VD = \frac{Line\ Loss}{Supply\ Voltage} \times 100$$

$$VD = \frac{5.59}{120} \times 100 = 4.66$$

$$VD = \textbf{4.66\%}$$

48. A 240 V, 1φ branch circuit with #8 Cu wire has a 35 A load. What is the length of the two-wire circuit? (Use approximate K.)

Ch 9, Table 8: #8 Cu = 16,510 CM

210.19(A)(1), FPN 4: 240 V × 3% = 7.2 V

Ch 9, Table 8: 1φ Cu = 25.8 Ω

$$D = \frac{CM \times VD}{K \times I}$$

$$D = \frac{16,510 \times 7.2}{25.8 \times 35}$$

$$D = \frac{118,872}{903} = 131.6$$

$$D = \textbf{131.6}'$$

49. A 240 V, 1ϕ branch circuit has a 200′ run of #4 Al wire. What is the amperage of the circuit? (Use approximate K.)

  Ch 9, Table 8: #4 Al = 41,740 CM
  210.19(A)(1), FPN 4: 240 V × 3% = 7.2 V
  Ch 9, Table 8: 1ϕ Al = 42.4 Ω

$$I = \frac{VD \times CM}{D \times K}$$

$$I = \frac{7.2 \times 41,740}{200 \times 42.4}$$

$$I = \frac{300,528}{8480} = 35.4$$

$$I = \textbf{35.4 A}$$

COST OF ENERGY

Electrical energy is provided by the local utility company. The energy used is recorded by a wattmeter. The unit for electrical power is the kilowatt (1000 W). The cost is based on kilowatt-hour (kWh) used. Rates are set by the local utility company.

The cost of energy is found by applying the formula:

$$Cost = \frac{T \times W \times Cost/kWh}{1000}$$

where
Cost = price (in dollars and cents)
T = time (in hours)
W = watts
Cost/kWh = price/kWh
1000 = constant

Examples: Cost of Energy

50. What is the cost for operating a 750 W electric heater for 8 hours at 8¢ per kWh?

$$Cost = \frac{T \times W \times Cost/kWh}{1000}$$

$$Cost = \frac{8 \times 750 \times .08}{1000} = .48$$

$$Cost = \textbf{48¢}$$

51. What is the cost for operating a 200 W lamp for 24 hours if the utility charge is 13¢ per kWh?

$$Cost = \frac{T \times W \times Cost/kWh}{1000}$$

$$Cost = \frac{24 \times 200 \times .13}{1000} = .62$$

$$Cost = \textbf{62¢}$$

TRANSPOSING FORMULAS

The journeyman electrician's exam generally provides base formulas for calculations. To solve for any variable, the base formula is transposed to isolate the variable on one side of the equation. For example, the Ohm's Law formula may be transposed to solve for either voltage, current, or resistance if the other two values are known.

  Base formula: $E = I \times R$
  where
  E = voltage (in V)
  I = current (in A)
  R = resistance (in Ω)

To solve for current, the base formula is transposed:

  Base formula: $E = I \times R$
  Divide each side by R (to cancel R from right side):

$$\frac{E}{R} = \frac{I \times R}{R}$$

  Final transposed formula: $\frac{E}{R} = I$
  or

$$I = \frac{E}{R}$$

Examples: Transposing Formulas

52. What is the formula for finding resistance when using Ohm's Law?

  Base formula: $E = I \times R$
  Divide each side by I (to cancel I from right side):

$$\frac{E}{I} = \frac{I \times R}{I}$$

  Final transposed formula: $\frac{E}{I} = R$
  or

$$R = \frac{E}{I}$$

53. What is the formula for finding current when using the voltage drop formula?

Base formula: $VD = \dfrac{K \times I \times D}{CM}$

Multiply each side by CM (to cancel CM from right side): $VD \times CM = (K \times I \times D)$

Divide each side by K (to cancel K from right side):

$\dfrac{VD \times CM}{K} = I \times D$

Divide each side by D (to cancel D from right side):

$\dfrac{VD \times CM}{K \times D} = I$

Final transposed equation: $\dfrac{VD \times CM}{K \times D} = I$

or

$I = \dfrac{VD \times CM}{K \times D}$

METRICS

The metric system is the most commonly used measurement system in the world. The English system is primarily used in the United States. The metric system is based on the meter (m), liter (l), and gram (g). The English system uses the inch (in. or ″), foot (ft or ′), pint (pt), gallon (gal.), ounce (oz), and pound (lb) as the basic units of measure. Conversion factors are used to change measurements from one system to the other.

English/Metric Conversion Factors

1 inch = 25.4 millimeters
1 inch = 2.54 centimeters
1 foot = .3048 meters
1 millimeter = 0.03937 inches
1 centimeter = 0.3937 inches
1 meter = 3.28084 feet

1 cubic inch = 16.387064 cubic centimeters
1 cubic centimeter = 0.061024 cubic inches
1 square millimeter = 0.001550 square inches
1 square inch = 645.16 square millimeters

Examples: Metrics

54. What is the diameter in inches of a light fixture with a diameter of 17.145 cm?
17.145 cm ÷ 2.54 = **6.75 or 6¾″**

55. What is the length in feet of a length of wire 50 m long?
50 m × 3.28084 = **164′**

56. What is the volume in cubic inches of a box with a volume of 295 cu cm?
295 cu cm × 0.061024 = **18 cu in.**

57. What is the diameter in inches of No. 10 solid copper wire that has a diameter of 2.588 mm?
2.588 mm × 0.03937 = **.102″**

58. What is the resistance of 10 m of #1 Cu wire in ohms per meter?
Ch 9, Table 8: resistance of #1 Cu wire = 0.505 Ω/km
0.505 ÷ 1000 = **0.000505 Ω/meter**

59. What is the resistance of 10 m of #1 Cu wire in ohms per foot.
10 m × 3.28084 = **32.8′**
Ch 9, Table 8: resistance of #1 Cu wire = 0.154 Ω/kft
0.154 ÷ 1000 = 0.000154 Ω/ft
0.000154 × 32.8′ = **0.005 Ω/ft**

60. What is the cross-sectional area in millimeters of a ½″ EMT conduit with a cross-sectional area of 0.622″?
0.622″ × 25.4 = **15.8 mm**

61. What is the cross-sectional area in inches of a ¾″ IMC conduit with a cross-sectional area of 377 sq mm?
377 sq mm × 0.001550 = **0.584 sq in.**

Name _____ Date _____

Electrical Formulas

_____ **1.** ___ is the horsepower rating of an electric motor.
A. Power factor %   C. Output
B. Torque   D. Input

_____ **2.** True power equals apparent power in an electrical circuit containing only ___.
A. resistance   C. inductance
B. capacitance   D. impedance

_____ **3.** The NEC® recommends a ___% VD for branch circuits.
A. 2   C. 125
B. 3   D. 5

_____ **4.** Water freezes at ___°C and boils at ___°C at sea level.
A. –23;212   C. –32;100
B. 0;212   D. 0;100

_____ **5.** ___ is the same in a parallel branch.
A. Current   C. Voltage
B. Resistance   D. VA

_____ **6.** An electrical circuit has a current of 25 A with a total resistance of 21 Ω. The true power of the circuit is ___ W.
A. 46   C. 13,125
B. 525   D. neither A, B, nor C

_____ **7.** The output of a 5 HP motor is ___ VA.
A. 150   C. 370
B. 1500   D. 3730

_____ **8.** An A/H has a 10 kW, 240 V, 1ϕ heat strip. The resistance of the heat strip is ___ Ω.
A. 41.6   C. 2.88
B. 576   D. 5.76

_____ **9.** The exact K for an uncoated #1 Cu conductor is ___ Ω.
A. 10.8   C. 12.6
B. 10.4   D. 12.88

_____ **10.** A 250 kcmil conductor has a circular mil area of ___.
A. .082   C. 250,000
B. .575   D. .0535

_____ 11. The cost of operating a 200 W lamp for 8 hours at 9′ per kWh is $___.
  - A. 1.44
  - B. 1.84
  - C. 0.44
  - D. 0.14

_____ 12. A circuit has a 4 Ω, 6 Ω, and 8 Ω resistor connected in series. The total resistance is ___ Ω.
  - A. 1.8
  - B. .542
  - C. 18
  - D. neither A, B, nor C

_____ 13. A circuit has a 4 Ω, 6 Ω, and 8 Ω resistor connected in parallel. The total resistance is ___ Ω.
  - A. 1.845
  - B. 18
  - C. .542
  - D. neither A, B, nor C

_____ 14. A 240 V, 1ϕ motor draws 28 A and is 55% efficient. The rating of the motor is ___ HP.
  - A. 2
  - B. 7½
  - C. 3
  - D. 5

_____ 15. The primary maximum overcurrent protection shall not exceed ___ A for a 1.5 kVA, 120/240 V, 1ϕ step-up transformer.
  - A. 20
  - B. 15
  - C. 10
  - D. neither A, B, nor C

_____ 16. A 40 A, 240 V, 1ϕ branch circuit has a 210′ run of #8 XHHW Al conductor rated at 75°C. The VD is ___ V. (Use approximate K.)
  - A. 7.2 V
  - B. 12 V
  - C. 15 V
  - D. neither A, B, nor C

_____ 17. The total resistance in a circuit that has a 3 Ω resistor connected in series with a 4 Ω and a 3 Ω resistor connected in parallel is ___ Ω.
  - A. 4.7
  - B. 13
  - C. 3.8
  - D. 6.5

_____ 18. The total resistance in a circuit that has a 6 Ω resistor connected in series with a 2 Ω, 5 Ω, and 10 Ω resistor connected in parallel is ___ Ω.
  - A. 23
  - B. 8.9
  - C. 7.25
  - D. 12

_____ 19. The ampacity of a ½″ × 4″ Al busbar is ___ A.
  - A. 1000
  - B. 1400
  - C. 700
  - D. 1250

_____ 20. The ampacity of a ¼″ × 4″ Cu busbar is ___ A.
  - A. 700
  - B. 1200
  - C. 1100
  - D. 1000

Name _____ Date _____

Electrical Formulas

_____ **1.** A 300 W, 130 V incandescent lamp draws ___ A.
     A. 3   B. 2.6
     C. 2.1   D. 2.3

_____ **2.** A circuit has 1.5 A of current through a 40 Ω resistor. The current is ___ A if the resistance is increased to 50 Ω.
     A. 1.5   C. 1.2
     B. 2   D. 2.6

_____ **3.** Three 8 Ω resistors are connected in series. The total resistance is ___ Ω.
     A. 24   C. 8
     B. 2.66   D. neither A, B, nor C

_____ **4.** Three 8 Ω resistors are connected in parallel. The total resistance is ___ Ω.
     A. 2.66   C. 8
     B. 24   D. neither A, B, nor C

_____ **5.** A 5 Ω and a 10 Ω resistor are connected in parallel. The total resistance is ___ Ω.
     A. 15   C. 50
     B. 3.33   D. neither A, B, nor C

_____ **6.** A 10 Ω heater draws 4 A from a power supply. The power supply is ___ V.
     A. 120   C. 40
     B. .4   D. neither A, B, nor C

_____ **7.** The unit for the measurement of work is the ___.
     A. Coulomb   C. foot-pound
     B. Farad   D. watt-hour

_____ **8.** A conducting material has a certain resistance at 30°C (___°F).
     A. 30   C. 86
     B. 68   D. 72

_____ **9.** The operating temperature of an insulation should not exceed 104°F (___°C).
     A. 40   C. 72
     B. 60   D. neither A, B, nor C

_____ **10.** Current is defined as the flow of ___.
     A. protons   C. ohms
     B. neutrons   D. electrons

_____ 11. The maximum recommended line loss for a 40 A, 240 V, 1φ branch circuit is ___ V.
  A. 12   C. 3.6
  B. 7.2   D. neither A, B, nor C

_____ 12. A 115 V, 1φ circuit has an 8 V line loss. The voltage drop is ___%.
  A. 14.38   C. 2.64
  B. 6.96   D. neither A, B, nor C

_____ 13. A transformer has a 300 W, 120 V primary and a 295 W, 12 V secondary. The transformer is ___% efficient.
  A. 95   C. 100
  B. 98   D. 80

_____ 14. With a source voltage of 120 V and a load of 6500 W, the voltage across the load reads 115 V. The power consumed by the conductors is ___ W.
  A. 283   C. 150
  B. 300   D. 75

_____ 15. The Joule is the measurement of ___.
  A. voltage   C. electrons
  B. energy   D. resistance

_____ 16. Electromotive force is ___.
  A. potential difference   C. work
  B. energy   D. Coulombs per second

_____ 17. A length of wire 60 m long equals ___'.
  A. 152.4   C. 197
  B. 145.4   D. 210

_____ 18. A length of conduit 24″ long equals ___ cm.
  A. 61   C. 78
  B. 7.31   D. 55.4

_____ 19. The total resistance of a circuit that has a 12 Ω resistor connected in series with six 12 Ω resistors connected in parallel is ___ Ω.
  A. 18   C. 14
  B. 8.9   D. 12.4

_____ 20. The total resistance of a circuit that has an 8 Ω resistor connected in series with 5 Ω, 7 Ω, and 9 Ω resistors connected in parallel is ___ Ω.
  A. 10.2   C. 29
  B. 7.1   D. 12

Name_____ Date _____

Electrical Formulas

A 1φ transformer with a 120 V primary and a 12 V secondary with a 300 W load is used for Problems 1 through 5.

_____ 1. The turns ratio of the transformer is ___.

      A. 1:10   C. 12:1

      B. 10:1   D. 1:2

_____ 2. The amperage of the secondary is ___ A.

      A. 2.5   C. 10

      B. 12   D. 25

_____ 3. The minimum rating required is ___ kVA.

      A. 3   C. .3

      B. 300   D. neither A, B, nor C

_____ 4. The primary current is ___ A.

      A. 25   C. 2.5

      B. 10   D. neither A, B, nor C

_____ 5. The resistance of the secondary winding is ___ Ω.

      A. 25   C. 2.5

      B. .48   D. neither A, B, nor C

_____ 6. ___ reduces copper losses.

      A. A silicon steel core   C. Increasing copper size

      B. Laminating the core   D. Using more windings

_____ 7. The neutral voltage for a 3φ, low-voltage, wye-connected transformer is ___V.

      A. 120   C. 208

      B. 240   D. 480

_____ 8. The high leg voltage for a low-voltage, delta-connected transformer is ___ V.

      A. 120   C. 208

      B. 240   D. 480

_____ 9. The Coulomb is the measurement of ___.

      A. voltage   C. electrons

      B. energy   D. resistance

A 3-wire, 120/240 V, 1φ branch circuit with two parallel loads is used for Problems 10 through 16. L1 to the neutral has a 120 V, 25 W load. L2 to the neutral has a 130 V, 100 W load. The neutral opens in the panel.

_____ **10.** The voltage applied to the loads is ___ V.
       A. 120   C. 240
       B. 130   D. either A, B, or C

_____ **11.** The resistance of the 25 W load is ___ Ω.
       A. 576   C. 9.6
       B. .208   D. neither A, B, nor C

_____ **12.** The resistance of the 100 W load is ___ Ω.
       A. 144   C. 2.4
       B. 169   D. .833

_____ **13.** The total resistance is ___ Ω.
       A. 745   C. 732
       B. 12   D. 1.041

_____ **14.** The amperage drawn on L1 conductor is ___ A.
       A. .16   C. .322
       B. 10   D. neither A, B, nor C

_____ **15.** The voltage drop across the 25 Ω load is ___ V.
       A. 120   C. 96
       B. 240   D. 185.5

_____ **16.** The voltage drop across the 100 W load is ___ V.
       A. 54.4   C. 144
       B. 130   D. 120

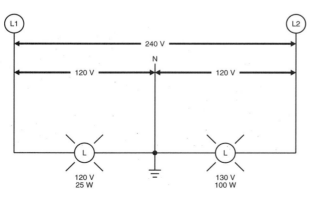

CIRCUIT NORMAL

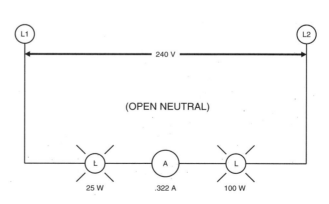

CIRCUIT WITH FAULT

Name _____ Date _____

Electrical Formulas

_____ 1. A 1 kVA, 1φ transformer has a 120 V primary drawing 8.33 A and a 240 V secondary drawing 3.9 A. The transformer is ___% efficient.

    A. 100   C. 94
    B. 85   D. neither A, B, nor C

_____ 2. A 7½ HP, 240 V, 1φ motor has an FLA of 40 A. The motor is ___% efficient.

    A. 70   C. 45
    B. 85   D. 58

_____ 3. An electrical circuit has 10 A of current and a resistance of 58 Ω. The voltage is ___ V.

    A. 48   C. 580
    B. 68   D. neither A, B, nor C

_____ 4. A #3 THW Cu, 3-wire, 120/240 V, 1φ feeder is 219′ long. The amperage available per phase is ___ A. (Use approximate K.)

    A. 100   C. 75
    B. 80   D. 67

_____ 5. A 4 Ω, 8 Ω, and 15 Ω resistor are connected in parallel. The total resistance is ___ Ω.

    A. 27   C. 8.6
    B. 3.25   D. 2.27

_____ 6. A 4 Ω resistor is connected in series with a 24 Ω and a 1 Ω resistor. The voltage drop across the 1 Ω resistor is 5 V. The supply voltage is ___ V.

    A. 145   C. 5
    B. 120   D. 105

_____ 7. The power needed for an 80% efficient, 5 HP, 240 V, 1φ motor is ___ VA.

    A. 3648   C. 2884
    B. 3730   D. 4662

_____ 8. A 10 kW, 240 V, 1φ load has an 85% power factor. The amperage drawn is ___ A.

    A. 41.6   C. 39.2
    B. 49   D. 118

_____ 9. A 15 kVA, 1φ load has a 240 V-rated source of supply. The amperage drawn is ___ A.

    A. 6.25   C. 50
    B. 68.1   D. 62.5

_____ **10.** A 21 A, 230 V, 1φ circuit with a power factor of 93% has ___ VA.

    A. 4830   C. 5193

    B. 213.9   D. 4492

_____ **11.** A 220 V series motor operating for ¾ of an hour has a current of 10 A. A total of ___ wH are used.

    A. 2933   C. 2200

    B. 1650   D. 75

_____ **12.** Electricity cost 12′ per kWH, how much will it cost to operate the motor in Problem 11?

    A. $19.80   C. 0.09¢

    B. $0.198   D. 35.4¢

_____ **13.** A 1φ transformer has a 120 V primary and a 12 V secondary. The transformer has a rated output of .5 kW and is 95% efficient. The primary power is ___ VA.

    A. 526   C. 475

    B. 500   D. neither A, B, nor C

_____ **14.** A 120 V heating element rated at 2200 W draws ___ A.

    A. 18.3   C. 20

    B. 1.83   D. 15

_____ **15.** ___ law states that the current in a circuit is proportional to the voltage and inversely proportional to the resistance.

    A. Lenz's   C. Kirchoff's

    B. Ohm's   D. Newton's

_____ **16.** A 10 Ω resistor has a voltage drop of 80 V and an unknown resistor. The supply voltage is 120 V. The resistance of the unknown resistor is ___ Ω.

    A. 5   C. 40

    B. 1.5   D. 8

_____ **17.** One conductor of a 120 V circuit for a 6.5 Ω heater has a resistance of .193 Ω. The total resistance of the complete circuit is ___ Ω.

    A. 6.5   C. 6.88

    B. 6.69   D. 12

_____ **18.** Four 4 Ω heaters are connected in parallel. The total resistance is ___ Ω.

    A. 16   C. 1

    B. 4   D. neither A, B, nor C

_____ **19.** True power equals apparent power when the power factor is ___.

    A. leading   C. 100%

    B. lagging   D. zero

_____ **20.** Opposition to the flow of electrons is ___.

    A. ohms   C. resistance

    B. voltage   D. current

NEC® Examples 4

This chapter contains examples of how the NEC® is applied. Each of the 74 questions and problems in this chapter is an example of applying the NEC® to solve electrical problems. The answers for all review questions are given in the back of this book. The answers for all sample licensing exams are given in the Answer Key. The NEC® references should be thoroughly studied.

CONDUIT FILL

Chapter 9, Tables and Examples contains requirements and mandatory rules for conduit fill. The various tables contain information to safely calculate conduit fill. Table 1 contains the percent fill of a conduit or raceway for a set amount of conductors. Chapter 9, Table 4 lists the trade sizes in standard inches and metric inches, internal diameter in inches, total area 100% sq in., and the amount of fill in sq in. based on the amount of conductors installed. This information is provided for different types of conduit and tubing.

Chapter 9, Table 5 lists the dimension of insulated conductors and fixture wire. This table gives the type, size, approximate diameter, and approximate area in sq in. *Note:* Pay close attention to *. Chapter 9, Table 5A covers compact aluminum conductors. A *compact conductor* is a conductor which has been compressed to eliminate voids between strands.

Annex C provides the maximum amount of conductors and fixtures wires that are permitted to be installed in different types of conduit or tubing. Tables C1 to C12 cover conductor and fixture wires of the same size and type of insulation for trade sizes from ⅜″ to 6″ conduit. *Note:* Pay close attention to *. Tables C1A through C12A cover compact conductors installed in different types of conduits or tubing. The tables are for conduit and tubing sizes when all conductors or fixture wires are the same size and have like insulation.

Examples: Conduit Fill

1. How many #12 THW Cu conductors can be installed in a ¾″ EMT conduit?

   Annex, Table C1: ¾″ = 11
   Conductors = **11**

2. What size RMC is required for three #12 THW Cu, three #12 TW Cu, three #12 RHW Cu (w/o outer covering), and three #8 THWN Cu conductors?

   Ch 9, Table 5:
3 #12 THW Cu	$.0181 \times 3 = .0543$
3 #12 TW Cu	$.0181 \times 3 = .0543$
3 #12 RHW Cu (w/o outer covering)	$.026 \times 3 = .078$
3 #8 THWN Cu	$.0366 \times 3 = \dfrac{.1098}{.2964}$

   Ch 9, Table 1; Ch 9, Table 4:
   ¾″ conduit = .220
   1″ conduit = .355
   RMC = **1″**

3. How many #12 THHN Cu conductors can be installed in a ½″ EMT conduit 23″ long?

   Ch 9, Note 4: Less than 24″ = 60% fill
   Ch 9, Table 4: 100% fill = .304
   $.304 \times .60 = .1824$

Ch 9, Table 5: THHN Cu = .0133

.1824 ÷ .0133 = 13.7

Ch 9, Note 7: Drop .7

Conductors = **13**

4. How many #8 TW Cu conductors can be installed in a ¾″ IMC conduit 12″ long?

Ch 9, Note 4: Less than 24″ = 60% fill

Ch 9, Table 4: 100% fill = .586

.586 × .60 = .3516

Ch 9, Table 5: #8 TW Cu = .0437

.3516 ÷ .0437 = 8

Conductors = **8**

5. What size rigid PVC, Schedule 40 is required for three #8 TW Cu phase conductors, one #10 TW Cu EGC, and one #8 stranded bare Cu conductor?

Ch 9, Table 5: 3 #8 TW Cu .0437 × 3 = .1311

1 #10 TW Cu .0243 × 1 = .0243

Ch 9, Table 8:

1 #8 bare Cu $.017 \times 1 = \frac{.017}{.1724}$

Ch 9, Table 1; Ch 9, Table 4: ¾″ = .203

PVC = **¾″**

6. How many #6 THW compact Al conductors can be installed in a 1¼″ flexible metal conduit?

Annex C, Table C3(A): 1¼″ = 7

Conductors = **7**

7. What size EMT is required for three #1/0 and one #1 XHHW Al compact conductors?

Ch 9, Table 5A:

3 #1/0 XHHW Al .1590 × 3 = .477

1 #1 XHHW Al $.1352 \times 1 = \frac{.1352}{.6122}$

Ch 9, Table 1; Ch 9, Table 4: 1½″ = .814

EMT = **1½″**

CONDUCTOR ADJUSTMENT FACTOR

The ampacities listed in Table 310.16 are based on three current-carrying conductors in a raceway. Chapter 9, Table C1 allows nine #12 THWN conductors in a ½″ raceway. Article 310.15 states that the allowable ampacity shall be reduced per the percentages listed in Table 310.15(B)(2)(a). When the number of current-carrying conductors exceeds three, the overcurrent protection shall be adjusted to reduce the allowable ampacity of the conductors. When the adjusted ampacity does not correspond to a standard rating under 800 A, the next higher standard rating is permitted. See 240.6.

The grounded (neutral) conductor that caries only unbalanced current shall not be counted for adjustment per 310.15(B)(4)(a). For a 3ɸ, 4-wire, wye system using two phases of the phase conductors, the neutral is considered a current-carrying conductor per 310.15(B)(4)(b). For a 3ɸ, 4-wire, wye system where the major portion of the load consists of nonlinear loads such as electric discharge lighting (ballast operated), the neutral is considered a current-carrying conductor per 310.15(B)(4)(c).

Examples: Conductor Adjustment

8. What is the ampacity of eight #8 THW 75°C Cu current-carrying conductors installed in a raceway?

Table 310.16: #8 THW 75°C = 50 A

50 A × .70 = 35 A

Ampacity = **35 A**

9. A piece of electrical equipment draws 35A. The raceway contains eight current-carrying conductors. What size THW 75°C Cu conductors are required?

Table 310.15(B)(2)(a):

$\frac{1}{.70} = 1.428$ (multiplier)

1.428 × 35 A = 49.98 A

Conductors = **#8 THW Cu**

10. What is the ampacity of four #12 THWN 75°C Cu current-carrying conductors installed in a 23″ raceway?

Table 310.16; 310.15(B)(2) Ex. 3:

#12 THWN 75°C Cu = 25 A

Ampacity = **25 A**

11. What is the ampacity of three #10 THW 75°C Cu current-carrying conductors and one #10 THW 75°C Cu EGC?

Table 310.16; 310.15(B)(2)(5):

#10 THWN 75°C Cu = 35 A

Ampacity = **35 A**

12. What is the ampacity of four #12 TW Cu conductors feeding three balanced resistive lighting circuits?

Table 310.16; 310.15(B)(4)(a):

#12 TW Cu = 25 A

Ampacity = **25 A**

13. A raceway contains four current-carrying conductors. A three-wire circuit (#12 THWN 75°C Cu) is derived from a 3ϕ, 4-wire, wye system. What is the ampacity?

> *Table 310.16; Table 310.15(B)(2)(a);*
> *310.15(B)(2)(4)(b):*
> #12 TW Cu = 25 A
> 25 A × .80 = 20 A
> *Ampacity = **20 A***

14. What is the ampacity of three incandescent lighting circuits fed from a 3ϕ, 4-wire, wye system using #12 THW 75°C Cu conductors?

> *Table 310.16; 310.15(B)(2)(4)(c):*
> #12 TW Cu = 25 A
> 25 A × .80 = 20 A
> *Ampacity = **20 A***

15. Five current-carrying #6 TW 75°C Cu conductors are required for resistive loads. What is the ampacity of the conductors and the maximum overcurrent protection permitted?

> *Table 310.16:*
> #6 TW Cu = 55 A
> 55 A × .80 = 44 A
> *Ampacity = **44 A***
> *240.4(B)(2)(3); 240.6:* Next higher size = 45 A
> OCPD = **45 A**

TEMPERATURE CORRECTION

A conductor shall not be used in such a manner that its operating temperature exceeds that designated for the type of insulated conductor per 310.10. Ampacities are based on an ambient temperature of 30°C (86°F). Ambient temperature is the temperature surrounding a device. Correction factors are applied for temperatures exceeding 30°C (86°F).

Examples: Temperature Correction

16. What is the ampacity of a 3-wire circuit using THW 75°C, #8 Cu conductors in an ambient temperature of 113°F?

> *Table 310.16:* #8 THW 75°C Cu = 50 A
> *Table 310.16, Correction Factors:* 113°F = .82
> .82 × 50 = 41 A
> *Ampacity = **41 A***

17. What size THW 75°C Cu conductors are required for a 3-wire circuit with a load of 41 A in an ambient temperature of 113°F?

> *Table 310.16, Correction Factors:* 113°F = .82
> $$\frac{1}{.82} = 1.2195 \text{ (multiplier)}$$
> 41 A × 1.2195 = 49.9 A
> .82 × 50 = 41 A
> *Conductors = **#8 THW 75°C Cu***

18. What is the ampacity of three #10 TW Cu conductors in an ambient temperature of 57°C?

> *Table 310.16:* Not listed for less than 60°C.
> *Ampacity = **Not Permitted***

SINGLE MOTORS 1ϕ (GENERAL DUTY)

Five factors that concern single motors are full-load current, conductor size, overloads, overcurrent protection, and disconnecting means.

Full-Load Current

The FLC for general duty motors shall be based on the HP and voltage ratings listed in Tables 430.247 through 430.250 per 430.6(A)(1). The FLC shall not be based on the motor's nameplate full-load current rating.

Example: Full-Load Current

19. What is the FLC of a 3 HP, 230 V, 1ϕ motor?

> *Table 430.248:* 3 HP, 230 V, 1ϕ = 17 A
> *FLC = **17 A***

Conductor Size

Branch-circuit conductors supplying a single motor shall have an ampacity not less than 125% of the motor full-load current rating per 430.22(A).

Example: Conductor Size

20. What is the minimum size THW 75°C Cu conductors required for a 3 HP, 230 V, 1ϕ motor?

> *Table 430.248:* 3 HP, 230 V, 1ϕ = 17 A
> *430.22(A):* 17 A × 125% = 21.25 A
> *Table 310.16:* THW 75°C Cu = 25 A
> *Conductors = **#12 THW Cu***

Overloads

A separate motor overload protection shall be based on the motor's nameplate full-load current rating per 430.6. *Overloads* are heat-sensing devices intended to protect the motor. Short circuits are not considered an overload. Note: Testing authority questions may not provide the nameplate rating for a motor. Therefore, use the FLC ratings listed in the Tables in 430 for overload calculations.

Examples: Overloads

21. In general, what is the maximum overload rating for a 3 HP, 230 V, 1ϕ motor?

Table 430.248: 3 HP, 230 V, 1ϕ = 17 A
430.32(A)(1): 17 A × 115% = 19.55 A
Maximum Overload Rating = **19.55 A**

22. A 3 HP, 230 V, 1ϕ motor has internal thermal protection. What is the maximum trip current rating?

Table 430.248: 3 HP, 230 V, 1ϕ = 17 A:
430.32(A)(2): 17 A × 156% = 26.52 A
Maximum Trip Current = **26.52 A**

23. A 3 HP, 230 V, 1ϕ motor has overloads sized per 430.32(A)(1). The motor starts, but fails to carry the load. What is the maximum overload permitted?

Table 430.248: 3 HP, 230 V, 1ϕ = 17 A
430.32(C): 17 A × 130% = 22.1 A
Maximum Overload = **22.1 A**

Overcurrent Protection

The starting current for a motor can be from 2 to 10 times the FLC, therefore the overcurrent protection must be sized to allow the motor to start. The overcurrent protection device is for protection against short circuits and ground-faults. The overcurrent protection device shall be capable of carrying the starting current 430.52. When ratings in Table 430.52 are not sufficient for the starting current of the motor, the percentages listed in 430.52(C), Ex. 2(a), (b), (c), and (d) may be applied.

Examples: Overcurrent Protection

24. What is the maximum size ITCB permitted when using a 3 HP, 230 V, 1ϕ motor with no code letter?

Table 430.248: 3 HP, 230 V, 1ϕ = 17 A
Table 430.52: ITCB = 250%
17 A × 250% = 42.5 A
430.52(C)(1), Ex. 1: 42.5 A
240.6: Next higher size = 45 A
Maximum Size ITCB = **45 A**

25. A 3 HP, 230 V, 1ϕ motor with no code letter has TDFs that are not sufficient for the starting current. What is the maximum size TDFs permitted?

Table 430.248: 3 HP, 230 V, 1ϕ = 17 A
430.52(C)(1), Ex. 2(b): 17 A × 225% = 38.25 A
Maximum Size TDFs = **35 A**

26. A 3 HP, 230 V, 1ϕ motor with no code letter has an ITCB that is not sufficient for starting the motor. What is the maximum size ITCB permitted?

Table 430.248: 3 HP, 230 V, 1ϕ = 17 A
430.52(C)(1), Ex. 2(c): 17 A × 400% = 68 A
Maximum Size ITCB = **60 A**

Disconnecting Means

A *disconnecting means* is a device that opens and closes phase conductors. They may, or may not, provide overcurrent protection (either fuses or CBs). The disconnecting means is the point at which personnel may turn OFF, lockout, and tagout power prior to maintenance. They are excellent points to take voltage and current measurements. Disconnecting means are covered in 430, Part I.

Example: Disconnecting Means

27. What is the minimum ampere rating for the disconnecting means for a 3 HP, 230 V, 1ϕ motor?

Table 430.248: 3 HP, 230 V, 1ϕ = 17 A
430.110(A): 17 A × 115% = 19.55 A
Minimum Ampere Rating = **19.55 A**

MOTOR FEEDERS

Conductors supplying several motors shall have ampacity at least equal to the sum of the FLC rating of all the motors, plus 25% of the highest-rated motor in the group per 430.24. The feeder protection device shall be based on the largest branch-circuit OCPD of the group plus the FLC ratings of the other motors per 430.62(A).

Examples: Motor Feeders

28. A 230 V, 1φ feeder is to supply 1 HP, 5 HP, and 7½ HP motors. What is the maximum size conductors using THW 75°C Cu?

Table 430.248:
1 HP FLA = 8 A
5 HP FLA = 28 A
7½ HP FLA = 40 A
430.24: 40 × 125% = 50 + 28 + 8 = 86 A
Table 310.16: #3 THW 75°C Cu = 100 A
Maximum Size Conductors = **100 A**

29. What is the maximum size ITCB required for feeder overcurrent protection in Problem 28?

Table 430.248: 7½ HP = 40 A
Table 430.52: 40 A × 250% = 100 A (standard size)
430.62: 100 A (largest OCPD of the group) + 28 A + 8 A = 136 A
240.6: Next smaller size = 125 A
Maximum Size ITCB = **125 A**

30. A 3-wire feeder supplies two 1 HP, 120 V motors and one 3 HP, 230 V motor. What are the maximum size conductors for the feeder using THW 75°C Cu?

Table 430.52: 3 HP, 230 V = 17 A × 125% = 21.25 A
1 HP, 120 V = 16 A

L1	N	L2
21 A	0	21 A
16 A	0	16 A
37 A	0	37 A

Table 310.16: #8 THW 75°C Cu = 50 A
Maximum Size Conductors = **50 A**

31. What is the maximum size TDFs required in Problem 30?

Table 430.52: 3 HP, 230 V = 17 A × 175% = 29.75 A
240.6: Next higher size = 30 A
30 A + 16 A = 46 A
240.6: Next lower size = 45 A
Maximum Size TDFs = **45 A**

RANGES (HOUSEHOLD)

Table 220.55 lists the demand factors for ranges. Actual load and demand load are very different. Demand factors are based on the diversified use of the range,

due to the fact that all parts of the range are not used at the same time.

Table 220.55, Column C is used for ranges that have a nameplate rating from 8¾ kW to 12 kW. For a range with a nameplate rating that falls between 8¾ kW and 12 kW, the demand load shall be computed at 8 kW. Refer to Note 1 when the 12 kW rating is exceeded.

Table 220.55, Column A is used for ranges with a nameplate rating less than 3½ kW. The nameplate rating is multiplied times the percentages listed in the Column to calculate the demand load.

Table 220.55, Column B is used for ranges with a nameplate rating that falls between 3½ kW and 8¾ kW. The nameplate rating is multiplied times the percentage listed in the Column to calculate the demand load.

Table 220.55, Note 1 states that the demand rating listed in Table 220.55, Column C shall be increased by 5% for every kW above 12 kW.

Table 220.55, Note 2 states that for ranges over 8¾ kW through 27 kW of different ratings, find the average range and apply Column C, increasing the values for every 5% 12 kW is exceeded. Use 12 kW for any range rated less than 12 KW.

Table 220.55, Note 3 grants permission to add the nameplate ratings of ranges that fall between 1¾ kW to 8¾ kW and multiply the total by the percentages listed in Column A or Column B for the number of appliances.

Table 220.55, Note 4 permits the branch-circuit load for a range to be based on Table 220.55. No demand is permitted for one wall-mounted oven or one counter-mounted cooking unit. The branch-circuit load shall be based on the nameplate rating of the unit.

One counter-mounted cooking unit and not more than two wall-mounted ovens are permitted to be treated as one range. Add the nameplate ratings of the units and use Column C.

Table 220.55, Note 5 permits the use of Table 220.55 for load calculations of household ranges used in a home-cooking class in a school.

For ranges 8¾ kW or more, the minimum branch-circuit rating shall be 40 A per 210.19(A)(3). For ranges 8¾ kW or higher, the ampacity of the neutral conductor shall not be less than 70%. The neutral conductor shall not be smaller than #10 per 210.19(A)(3), Ex 2.

The maximum unbalanced load of a feeder supplying a household range shall be considered as 70% of the load on the ungrounded conductors per 220.61(B).

Examples: Ranges

32. What is the demand load for one 10 kW range?
Table 220.55, Col C: 8 kW
Demand Load = **8 kW**

33. What is the demand load for a 3 kW range?
Table 220.55, Col A:
   3000 W × 80% = 2400 W = 2.4 kW
Demand Load = **2.4 kW**

34. What is the demand load for an 8 kW range?
Table 220.55, Col B:
   8000 W × 80% = 6400 W = 6.4 kW
Demand Load = **6.4 kW**

35. What is the demand load for a 13 kW range?
Table 220.55, Col C: 13 kW – 12 kW = 1 kW
Table 220.55, Note 1:
   8000 W × 105% = 8400 W = 8.4 kW
Demand Load = **8.4 kW**

36. What is the demand load for five 3 kW ranges?
Table 220.55, Col A:
   5 × 3000 W × 62% = 9300 W = 9.3 kW
Demand Load = **9.3 kW**

37. What is the demand load for five 7 kW ranges?
Table 220.55, Col B:
   5 × 7000 W × 45% = 15,750 W = 15.75 kW
Demand Load = **15.75 kW**

38. What is the demand load for five 9 kW ranges?
Table 220.55, Col C: 20 kW
Demand Load = **20 kW**

39. What is the demand load for five 15 kW ranges?
Table 220.55, Col C: 15 kW – 12 kW = 3 kW
Table 220.55, Note 1:
   20,000 W × 115% = 23,000 W = 23 kW
Demand Load = **23 kW**

40. A 9 kW, 240 V range is to be wired using TW Cu conductors. What are the minimum sizes permitted for the ungrounded conductors, grounded conductors, and the overcurrent protection?

Ungrounded Conductors
Table 220.55, Col. C: 8000 kW 240 V = 33.3 A
Table 310.16: 33.3 A = #8 TW Cu
Ungrounded Conductors = **#8 TW Cu**
Grounded Conductors
210.19(A)(3), Ex. 2: #10 TW Cu
Grounded Conductors = **#10 TW Cu**
OCPD
210.19(A)(3): 33.3 A requires 40 A
OCPD = **40 A**

41. What branch-circuit current rating is required for a 240 V, 12 kW range?

Table 220.55, Col C; Table 220.55, Note 4:
$$\frac{8000 \text{ W}}{240 \text{ V}} = 33.3 \text{ A } (210.19(A)(3))$$

Branch-Circuit Current Rating = **40 A**

42. What branch-circuit current rating is required for one 6 kW countertop unit and two 4 kW wall ovens are wired on the same 240 V branch-circuit?

Table 220.55, Note 4:
   6 kW + 4 kW + 4 kW = 14 kW
Table 220.55, Col C; 210.19(A)(3):
   8 kW × 110% = 8800 W 240 V = 36.6 A
Branch-Circuit Current Rating = **40 A**

43. What is the neutral load for five 12 kW ranges?

Table 220.55 Col C: Five 12 kW ranges = 20 kW
   220.61(B): 20 kW × 70% = 14 kW
Neutral Load = **14 kW**

44. What is the demand load for five 10 kW ranges, five 12 kW ranges, and five 14 kW ranges?

Table 220.55, Col C; Table 220.55, Note 2:
   5 × 12 = 60
   5 × 12 = 60
   <u>5 × 14 = 70</u>
15 ranges = 190 kW
   190 kW ÷ 15 = 12.6 kW (.6 major fraction)
Table 220.55, Col C: 15 ranges = 30 kW
   30 kW × 1.05 = 31.5 kW (.5 is not permitted to be dropped)
Demand Load = **31.5 kW**

CALCULATING BOX FILL FOR CONDUCTORS

Table 314.16(A) lists standard boxes. Standard boxes are not required to be marked with a cubic inch capacity. Boxes 100 cu in. or less not listed in the table, including plastic boxes, are required to be marked with their cubic inch capacity. Table 314.16(A) lists the minimum cubic inch capacity and the maximum number of the same size conductors permitted to be installed for the different types and sizes of boxes. The total volume of a box is based on the total volume of assembled sections, such as plaster rings, box extensions, etc. Table 314.16(A) is based on an empty box with no assembled sections. The following deductions from the conductor count listed in the table must be made:

A. Each ungrounded conductor and grounded conductor counts as one deduction.

B. A conductor that passes through a box without splice counts as one deduction.

C. A box that contains one or more cable clamps requires one deduction.

D. A box that contains a hickey or a fixture stud requires one deduction.

E. Each yoke or fixture strap with one or more devices requires a deduction of two (an S/P switch and a duplex receptacle would require a deduction of two).

F. The total amount of all equipment grounding conductors count as one deduction.

Ex. An equipment grounding conductor and not over four luminaire (fixture) wires smaller than #14 AWG are permitted to be omitted from the calculations.

Table 314.16(B) is used for calculating box fill with different size conductors. The same deductions (A through F) including the exception apply. The deductions must be based on the largest conductor size entering the box.

Examples: Box Fill

45. How many #12 conductors are permitted in a 4″ sq 1½″ box?
Table 314.16 (A): **nine conductors**

46. How many #14 conductors may be added to a device box 3″ × 2″ × 3½″ that contains an S/P switch, two cable clamps, and a 14/2 W/grd Type MN cable?

Deductions
S/P switch: 2
Two cable clamps: 1
Two #14 conductors: 2
Grounding conductor: 1
Total deductions: 6
   Table 314.16 (A): 3″ × 2″ × 3½″ device box = nine #14 conductors
   9 – 6 = 3
Three #14 conductors may be added

47. What is the minimum cubic inch volume required for a box that contains three #12 conductors and one #12 equipment grounding conductor, and four #14 and three #10 conductors with one equipment grounding conductor?
   Table 314.16(B): #12 - 3 × 2.25 = 6.75; #14 - 4 × 2.00 = 8; #10 - 3 × 2.50 = 7.5; equipment ground = 2.5
Total volume required = **24.75 cu in.**

48. What is the minimum cubic inch volume required for a box that contains two cable clamps, one 14/2 W/grd Type NM cable, one 10/2 W/grd Type NM cable, a duplex receptacle, and three #16 fixture wires?
   Cable clamps: 1 × 2.5 = 2.5; #14 conductor: 2 × 2 = 4; #10 conductor: 2 × 2.5 = 5; receptacle: 2 × 2.5 = 5; equipment grounds: 1 × 2.5 = 2.5 Fixture wire (omit): = 0
Total volume required = **19 cu in.**

CONDUCTOR RESISTANCE

Chapter 9, Table 8 is used to find the resistance values of conductors. *Resistance* is opposition to the flow of electrons. The unit of measurement for resistance is the Ohm (Ω). The cross-sectional area of wire is commonly expressed in square inches. Electrical conductors are expressed in circular mils. The American Wire Gauge (AWG) is a standard for wire sizes. Four factors that affect the resistance of conductors are:

- Size: Cross-sectional area measured in circular mils (cm)
- Type of Material: Cu or Al
- Length: Ω/kFT
- Temperature: DC resistance at 75°C (167°F)

Size. The size of a conductor affect the resistance. The resistance of a wire is inversely proportional to its cross-sectional area. For example, for a ¼″ OD conductor, the resistance is four times greater than the resistance of a ½″ OD conductor. As the conductor size increases, the resistance decreases.

Type of Material. The type of material of a conductor affects the resistance. If the type of material for conductors with the same cross-sectional area and the same length differ, the resistance also differs. For example, the resistance for 1000′ of #12 Cu conductor is 1.93 Ω. The resistance for 1000′ of #12 Al conductor is 3.18 Ω. See Chapter 9, Table 8.

Length. The length of a conductor affects the resistance. The shorter the conductor, the less the resistance. The longer the conductor, the more the resistance. For example, the resistance for 1000′ of #12 Cu conductor is 1.93 Ω. The resistance for 2000′ of #12 Cu conductor is 3.86 Ω.

Temperature. The temperature of a conductor affects the resistance. The resistance of all conductors increase as the temperature of the conductor increases. The resistance values of Chapter 9, Table 8 are based on 75°C (167°F).

Examples: Conductor Resistance

49. What is the area in circular mills of a #14 Cu, solid, uncoated, bare conductor?

Ch 9, Table 8: 4110 CM

*Area = **4110 CM***

50. What is the diameter of a #14 Cu, solid, uncoated, bare conductor?

Ch 9, Table 8: .064″

*Diameter = **.064″***

51. What is the resistance of a #14 Cu, solid, uncoated, bare conductor per 1000′?

Ch 9, Table 8: 3.07 Ω

*Resistance = **3.07 Ω***

52. What is the cross-sectional area of a #14 Cu, solid, uncoated, bare conductor in sq in.?

Ch 9, Table 8: .003 sq in.

*Area = **.003 sq in.***

53. What is the resistance of 125′ of solid, #10 THW Al wire?

Ch 9, Table 8:

$$\#10 \ \Omega/kFT = \frac{2}{1000} = .002 \ \Omega/ft$$

$$.002 \times 125' = .25 \ \Omega$$

*Resistance = **.25 Ω***

54. What is the length of solid #8 Cu with a resistance of .24 Ω?

Ch 9, Table 8:

$$\#8 \ \Omega/kFT = \frac{.764}{1000} = .000764 \ \Omega/ft$$

$$\frac{.24}{.00764} = 314'$$

*Length = **314′***

55. What is the total resistance per 1000′ of a parallel set of #2/0 Cu conductors?

Ch 9, Table 8:

$$\# \ 2/0 \ \Omega/kFT = .0967$$

$$R_T = \frac{R_1}{N} = \frac{.0967}{2} = .04835 \ \Omega$$

*Total Resistance = **.04835 Ω***

ELECTRIC WELDERS

Article 630 covers individual welders. Subsections 630.11(A) and (B) cover ampacity for supply conductors for arc welders.

Supply conductors shall not be less than the I_{1eff} value on the welder nameplate. If no I_{1eff} is listed, the ampacity of the supply conductors shall be determined by multiplying the rated primary current in amperes listed on the nameplate and the duty cycle multiplier for the arc welder.

Overcurrent protection shall be rated at not more than 200% of the I_{1max} (the maximum amount of rated supply current at the maximum rated output) or the rated primary current of the arc welder. Section 630.12 permits using the next higher standard rating (240.6).

Examples: Welders

56. An AC and DC TIG or stick welder has a rated output of 300 A, 30 V, with a 60% duty cycle. The input current is 91 A with a 208 V source of supply.

What is the ampacity required for the supply conductors?

> Subsection 630.11(A)
> Primary current = 91 A
> Duty cycle = 60%
> Multiplier = .78
> 91 A × .78 = 70.98 A
> Ampacity of supply conductors = **71 A**

57. A DC motor-generator arc welder has a 230 V, 3ϕ, 78 A input. The output is 400 A/36 V with a 60% duty cycle. What is the ampacity of the supply conductors?

> Subsection 630.11(A)
> Primary current = 78 A
> Duty cycle = 60%
> Multiplier = .81
> 78 A × .81 = 63.18 A
> Ampacity of supply conductors = **63 A**

58. A resistance spot welder has a rated output of 10 kVA with a 50% duty cycle. The input rating is 220 V/45 A. What is the ampacity required for the supply conductors?

> Subsections 630.31(A)(1) and (2)
> Primary current = 45 A
> Duty cycle = 50%
> Multiplier = .71
> 45 A × .71 = 31.95 A
> Ampacity of supply conductors = **32 A**

59. A DC welder with capability of stick and TIG welding in addition to air carbon arc gouging has an output of 250 A/30 V with a 50% duty cycle. The machine has a 460 V, 1ϕ supply drawing 33 A. What is the maximum rating of the OCPD?

> Subsection 630.12(A)
> 33 A × 200% = 66 A
> Cannot exceed 200%. Next lower standard rating shall be used per 240.6
> Maximum OCPD rating = **60 A**

SERVICE CALCULATIONS (RESIDENTIAL)

Articles 310.15(B)(6) and Table 310.15(B)(6) permit a reduction in the size of service entrance conductors for a dwelling unit when the nominal voltage is 120/240 V. Table 310.15(B)(6) can be used only for 120/240 V distribution systems. The grounded (neutral) conductor is permitted to be smaller than the ungrounded (hot) conductor. The GEC is a critical connection and must meet all requirements per 250. If the ungrounded (neutral) conductor and the GEC open, serious electrical damage could occur in the dwelling unit.

Examples: Service Calculations

60. A dwelling has a 300 A, 120/240 V, 1ϕ service with THW Al conductors. What are the sizes for the ungrounded and grounded conductors?

> *Ungrounded Conductors*
> *Table 310.15(B)(6):*
> 300 A requires 350 kcmil
> *Ungrounded Conductors =* **350 kcmil**
> *Grounded Conductors*
> *Note 3 of Notes to Ampacity Tables of 0 to 2000 Volts:*
> Generally permitted to drop
> two AWG sizes = 250 kcmil
> *Grounded Conductors =* **350 kcmil**

Article 310.15(B) permits the grounded conductor to be smaller than the ungrounded conductor. This requires a load calculation. Generally, contractors size all service entrance conductors the same.

61. An apartment building has a 120/208 V, 3ϕ, 4-wire service with a 100 A, 120/208 V, 1ϕ feeder of THW Cu to each apartment. What are the sizes for the ungrounded and grounded conductor to each apartment?

> *Ungrounded Conductor*
> *Table 310.16:* 100 A requires #3
> *Ungrounded Conductor =* **#3**
> *Grounded Conductor*
> *310.15(B)(4)(b):* 100 A requires #3
> *Grounded Conductor =* **#3**

Article 310.15(B)(4)(b) states that the neutral conductor, when using two phases of a 3ϕ, 4-wire, wye system, carries approximately the same current as the other conductors.

62. The GES in Problem 60 is an underground water pipe. What size Cu GEC is required?

> *Table 250.66:* 350 kcmil requires #2 Cu
> *GEC =* **#2 Cu**

The GEC is based on the largest service entrance conductor per Table 250.66.

63. The grounding electrode in Problem 60 is a concrete-encased electrode. What size Cu GEC is required?

250.52(A)(3): Not required to be larger than #4 Cu

GEC = **#4 Cu**

SERVICE LOAD CALCULATIONS (OPTIONAL CALCULATION–220.82)

Article 220 permits two methods for computing service entrance loads for a dwelling unit. Section I is general information. Sections II and III are used for the standard and optional methods for calculating service entrance loads and conductor sizes. The Optional Calculation is a quick and simple method to use. It is the most common method used for computing service entrance loads for dwellings, although the loads may calculate slightly higher than with the Standard Calculation. See 220.82. Annex D of the NEC® shows examples for each method.

Examples: Optional Calculation

Use for Problems 64 through 72.

A dwelling unit has a 50′ × 42′ floor area with a 320 sq ft attached garage. The dwelling unit has a 13 kW range, 4.5 kW hot water heater, 5 kW electric dryer, ⅓ HP garbage disposal, 1.2 kW dishwasher, and a 40 A, 240 V heat pump with 10 kW of supplemental heat. No system interlock. The service is 120/240 V, 1ɸ.

64. What is the general lighting load (Optional Calculation)?

220.82(B)(1): 50′ × 42′ × 3 VA = 6300 VA

General Lighting Load = **6300 VA**

Allow 3 VA per sq ft for general lighting and general-use receptacles per 220.82(B)(1). The floor area is computed from the outside dimensions of the dwelling. For dwelling units, the computed floor area does not include open porches, garages, or unused or unfinished spaces not adaptable for future use per 220.12.

65. How many 15 A, 2-wire circuits are required for general lighting (Optional Calculation)?

$$I = \frac{P}{E}$$

$$I = \frac{6300}{120} = 52.5$$

$$\frac{52.5}{15} = 3.5 \text{ (round to 4)}$$

Two-wire Circuits = **4**

All general-use receptacle outlets of 20 A or less in dwelling units (except for small appliance and laundry outlets) shall be considered for general illumination. No additional load calculations shall be required for such outlets per 220.14(J).

66. What is the calculated load for the ungrounded (hot) conductors (Optional Calculation)? See 220.82 and Appd D, Example D2(c).

220.82(B)(1): General Lighting:

50′ × 42′ × 3 VA/sq ft	= 6300 VA

220.82(B)(2):

Small Appliance & Laundry:	
1500 VA × 2 + 1500 VA	= 4500 VA

220.82(B)(3):

Range	= 13,000 VA
Hot Water Heater	= 4500 VA
Dryer	= 5000 VA

220.82(B)(4): Table 430.248:

Food Waste Disposer:	
7.2 A × 120 V	= 864 VA

220.82(B)(3):

Dishwasher	= 1200 VA
Total	= 35,364 VA

Applying Demand Factors

220.82(B): 100% of first 10 kVA = 10,000 VA

Over 10 kVA × 40%

35,364 VA – 10,000 VA = 25,364 VA

25,364 VA × 40% = 10,146 VA

10,000 VA + 10,146 VA = 20,146 VA

Demand Load Without A/C and Heat = 20,146 VA

220.82(C)(2): Heat Pump and Supplementary Heat have no system interlock, 100% nameplate rating:

Heat Pump = 40 A × 240 V = 9600 VA

Supplementary Heat = 10,000 VA

9600 VA + 10,000 VA = 19,600 VA

Annex D, Example D2(c)

Demand Lad of Heat Pump with

$$\textit{Supplementary Heat} = \frac{19,600 \text{ VA}}{39,746 \text{ VA}}$$

$$Load = \frac{39,746 \text{ VA}}{240 \text{ V}} = 166 \text{ A}$$

Calculated Load for Ungrounded Conductors = **166 A**

67. What is the minimum size service and service entrance conductors using THW Cu conductors (Optional Calculation)?

Calculated Load for Ungrounded Conductors = 166 A

Table 310.15(B)(6)

Minimum Size Service = **200 A**

Service Entrance Conductors

Ungrounded Conductor = **#2/0 THW Cu**

Grounded Conductor = **#2/0 THW Cu**

68. What is the calculated load for the grounded (neutral) conductor (Standard Calculation)?

The neutral load is computed per 220, Sections I and II. In general, the maximum unbalance shall be the maximum net computed load between the neutral and any one hot conductor per 220.61. To calculate the maximum unbalance, all loads connected to the neutral shall be computed. See Annex D, Examples D1(a), D1(b), D2(a), and D2(b). There is no Optional Calculation method for calculating neutral loads.

220.40, Table 220.42: General Lighting:

50' × 42' × 3 VA/sq ft	= 6300 VA

220.52(A)(B): Small Appliance and Laundry:

1500 VA × 3	= 4500 VA
	10,800 VA
Applying Demand Factors	

Table 220.42: First 3000 VA

or less × 100%	= 3000 VA
Next 3001 VA to 120,000 VA × 35%	
10,800 VA – 3000 VA =	
7800 VA × 35%	= 2730 VA
General Lighting and Small	
Appliance Load	= 5730 VA

Table 220.55; 220.61(B): Range:

8400 VA × 70%	= 5880 VA
220.61(B): Dryer: 5000 VA × 70%	= 3500 VA
220.53: 1200 VA Dishwasher	= 1200 VA
220.53: 864 VA Food Waste Disposer	= 864 VA
	17,174 VA

$$Load = \frac{17,174 \text{ VA}}{240 \text{ V}} = 71.55 \text{ or } 72$$

Calculated Load for Grounded Conductor = **72 A**

69. What is the total load for a dwelling with a central A/C unit drawing 30 A at 240 V, 1φ with a 10 kW, 240 V, 1φ central space-heating (Optional Calculation)?

220.82(C)(1): 100% nameplate rating of A/C:

30 A × 240 V = 7200 VA

220.82(C)(4): 65% nameplate rating of heat:

10,000 VA × 65% = 6500 VA

Demand Load Without A/C and Heat =	20,146 VA
220.60: Largest Load: A/C	= 7200 VA
	27,346 VA

$$Load = \frac{27,346 \text{ VA}}{240 \text{ V}} = 114 \text{ A}$$

Total Load = **114 A**

70. What is the total load for a dwelling with a central 40 A, 240 V, 1φ AC and 15 kW, 240 V, 1φ central electric space heating (Optional Calculation)?

220.82(C)(1): 100% nameplate rating of A/C:

40 A × 240 V = 9600 VA

220.82(C)(4): 65% nameplate rating of heat:

5,000 VA × 65% = 9750 VA

Demand Load Without A/C and Heat =	20,146 VA
220.60: Largest Load: Heat	= 9750 VA
	29,896 VA

$$Load = \frac{29,896 \text{ VA}}{240 \text{ V}} = 125 \text{ A}$$

Total Load = **125 A**

71. What is the total load for a dwelling with no air conditioning and three separately controlled 2 kW, 240 V, 1φ electric space heating units (Optional Calculation)?

220.82(C)(5): 65% nameplate rating of heat:

3 × 2000 VA × 65%	= 3900 VA
Demand Load Without A/C and Heat	= 20,146 VA
	24,046 VA

$$Load = \frac{24,046 \text{ VA}}{240 \text{ V}} = 100 \text{ A}$$

Total Load = **100 A**

72. What is the total load for a dwelling with no air conditioning and five 1.5 kW, 240 V, 1φ separately controlled space heating units (Optional Calculation)?

220.82(C)(6): 40% nameplate rating of heat:

5 × 1500 VA × 40%	= 3000 VA
Demand Load Without A/C and Heat =	20,146 VA
	23,146 VA

$$Load = \frac{23,416 \text{ VA}}{240 \text{ V}} = 96 \text{ A}$$

Total Load = **96 A**

SERVICE LOAD CALCULATIONS (STANDARD CALCULATION–220, PARTS A AND B)

The Standard Calculation for calculating the service entrance loads for a dwelling unit is more difficult to use than the Optional Calculation. Service entrance loads computed by the Standard Calculation generally require a larger service than service entrance loads calculated by the Optional Calculation.

Examples: Standard Calculations

Use for Problems 73 and 74.

A dwelling unit has a floor area of 2,700 sq ft with a 12 kW range, 1.2 kW dishwasher, 4.5 kW hot water heater, 4.8 kW dryer, 864 W garbage disposal, 1.5 kW garage door opener, and a 40 A central A/C unit. The service is 120/240 V, 1ϕ.

73. What is the general lighting load (Standard Calculation)?

Table 220.12: General Lighting:

2,700 VA × 3 VA/sq ft	= 8100 VA
220.52(A): Small Appliance:	
1500 VA × 2	= 3000 VA
220.52(B): Laundry: 1500 VA	= 1500 VA
	12,600 VA

Applying Demand Factors

Table 220.42: First 3000 VA or less × 100% = 3000 VA

3001 VA to 120,000 VA × 35% =	
9600 VA × 35%	= 3360 VA
	6360 VA

General Lighting Load = **6360 VA**

74. What is the calculated load for the ungrounded (hot) conductors (Standard Calculation)?

220.12: General Lighting Load	= 6360 VA
Table 220.55, Col C: Range	= 8000 VA
220.53: Dishwasher: 1.2 kVA × 75%	= 900 VA
Hot Water Heater: 4.5 kVA × 75%	= 3375 VA
Garbage Disposal: 864 VA × 75%	= 648 VA
Garage Door Opener: 1.5 kVA × 75%	= 1125 VA
Air Conditioning: 40 A × 240 V	= 9600 VA
220.54: Dryer: 5000 VA	= 5000 VA
	35,008 VA

$$Load = \frac{35,008 \text{ VA}}{240 \text{ V}} = 146 \text{ A}$$

Calculated Load for Ungrounded Conductors = **146 A**

Name _____ Date _____

NEC® Examples

_____ **1.** In designing circuits, the current-carrying capacity of conductors should be corrected for heat at room temperatures above ___°F.
    A. 30   C. 72
    B. 86   D. 90

_____ **2.** The most common type of CB is ___.
    A. instantaneous   C. impedance type
    B. inverse time   D. power factor type

_____ **3.** In general, ampacity for single motors is based on the ___.
    A. nameplate rating   C. armature amps
    B. locked-rotor amps   D. neither A, B, nor C

_____ **4.** When determining the load on the VA/sq ft basis, the floor area shall be computed from the ___ dimensions of the building.
    A. outside   C. either A or B
    B. inside   D. neither A nor B

_____ **5.** The fill capacity of a nipple not exceeding 24″ in length is ___%.
    A. 100   C. 70
    B. 40   D. 60

_____ **6.** ___ #12 XF conductors can be installed in a ½″ EMT conduit.
    A. Four   C. Six
    B. Seven   D. Eight

_____ **7.** ___ #12 RHW conductors without outer covering can be installed in a 1″ RMC raceway.
    A. Thirteen   C. Eight
    B. Nine   D. Seven

_____ **8.** The derating percentage for eleven current-carrying conductors is ___%.
    A. 50   C. 80
    B. 0   D. 70

_____ **9.** The cross-sectional area of 1½″ liquidtight flexible metal conduit is ___ sq in.
    A. 1.981   C. 1.610
    B. 1.588   D. 2.017

_____ **10.** ___ is ambient temperature.
    A. Temperature surrounding installations   C. Outside temperature
    B. Room temperature   D. either A, B, or C

_____ 11. A bare #4 Cu conductor may be concrete-encased and serve as the GEC when at least ___′ in length.

    A. 25   C. 10

    B. 15   D. 20

_____ 12. The area of a #12 RHW conductor without outer covering is ___ sq in.

    A. .0135   C. .0230

    B. .0206   D. .026

_____ 13. The diameter of a #10 solid aluminum conductor is ___″.

    A. .011   C. .102

    B. .008   D. neither A, B, nor C

_____ 14. Generally, branch-circuit conductors supplying a single motor shall have an ampacity not less than ___% of the motor FLC rating.

    A. 110   C. 125

    B. 115   D. 200

_____ 15. ___ THWN service-entrance conductors are permitted for a 100 A, 120/240 V, 1ϕ service for a dwelling.

    A. #3 Cu   C. #4 Cu

    B. #1 Al   D. #1 Cu

_____ 16. Ten general-purpose receptacles added to a dwelling increases the service load by ___ VA.

    A. 0   C. 3240

    B. 1620   D. neither A, B, nor C

_____ 17. Fire protection emergency systems in assembly occupancies for not less than ___ people shall meet additional requirements.

    A. 100   C. 200

    B. 150   D. 1000

_____ 18. FCC cable shall be covered with carpet squares not larger than ___ sq in.

    A. 36   C. 30

    B. 24   D. 12

_____ 19. A single conductor cable installed in cable tray shall be larger than #___ AWG.

    A. 1   C. 2/0

    B. 1/0   D. 3/0

_____ 20. An enclosure for a receptacle out of doors is installed in a flush-mounted box in a finished surface. The faceplate assembly must provide a ___ connection between the plate and the finished surface.

    A. raintight   C. waterproof

    B. rainproof   D. watertight

Name _____ Date _____

NEC® Examples

_____ **1.** A rating of ___ A is not a standard rating for a fuse.
    A. 15   C. 75
    B. 20   D. 125

_____ **2.** There are ___ conductor strands in #1/0 THHN Al wire.
    A. 7   C. 15
    B. 10   D. 19

_____ **3.** The minimum branch circuit rating for an 8¾ kW household range shall be ___ A.
    A. 40   C. 30
    B. 35   D. 50

_____ **4.** The diameter of bare #10 Cu stranded conductor is ___".
    A. 0.102   C. 0.168
    B. 0.116   D. 0.199

_____ **5.** The FLC of a 5 HP, 208 V, 1φ motor is ___ A.
    A. 15.2   C. 28
    B. 16.72   D. 30.8

_____ **6.** The short-circuit protection for the motor in Problem #5, using an ITCB, normally may not exceed ___ A.
    A. 40   C. 70
    B. 60   D. 80

_____ **7.** If the nameplate of the motor in Problem 5 reads 28 A, ___ A is the value used to determine the overload protection.
    A. 28   C. 38.5
    B. 30.8   D. neither A, B, nor C

_____ **8.** The length of uncoated, stranded #12 Cu conductor with a resistance of .41 Ω is ___'.
    A. 207   C. 108
    B. 432   D. 500

_____ **9.** The maximum size ITCB allowed for A 120/240 V, 1φ, 3-wire feeder that powers a 3 HP, 240 V, 1φ motor and two 1 HP, 240 V, 1φ motors is ___ A.
    A. 45   C. 50
    B. 35   D. 60

_____ **10.** The minimum allowable ampacity for the feeder conductors in Problem 9 is ___ A.
    A. 29   C. 33
    B. 37   D. neither A, B, nor C

_____ **11.** The ampacity of a #6 RHW Al conductor in a room temperature of 47°C is ___ A.
      A. 50   C. 41
      B. 37.5   D. 49.2

_____ **12.** The maximum size OCPD permitted for #10 TW Cu conductor in a 1″ conduit 23″ long with a total of 11 current-carrying conductors in an ambient temperature of 28°C is ___ A.
      A. 15   C. 25
      B. 20   D. 30

_____ **13.** The branch circuit load for a 12 kW household range is ___ kW.
      A. 12   C. 8
      B. 15   D. 10

_____ **14.** The ampacity for a 3 HP, 240 V, 1ϕ motor is ___ A.
      A. 17   C. 18.7
      B. 21   D. 25.5

_____ **15.** The total demand load for eight 14 kW, five 8 kW, and ten 12 kW household ranges is ___ kW.
      A. 39.9   C. 292
      B. 38   D. neither A, B, nor C

_____ **16.** The ampacity of a #1, RHW, 167°F, Al conductor in a room temperature of 59°C is ___ A.
      A. 100   C. 71
      B. 67   D. 58

_____ **17.** An autotransformer rated less than 600 V shall have the overcurrent protection set at not more than ___% of the full-load input current of the transformer.
      A. 110   C. 125
      B. 115   D. 250

_____ **18.** Overhead conductors other than those required for the amusement ride itself shall be maintained at a clearance of ___′ in any direction.
      A. 10   C. 25
      B. 15   D. 50

_____ **19.** The interior of a spray painting booth is a ___ location.
      A. Class I, Division 1   C. Class II, Division 1
      B. Class I, Division 2   D. Class III, Division 1

_____ **20.** Temporary wiring on a construction site shall be removed ___ upon completion of the project.
      A. within 30 days   C. within 60 days
      B. within 7 days   D. immediately

Name _____ Date _____

NEC® Examples

_____ **1.** The load is calculated at ___ VA for a dwelling with a 30 A, 240 V, 1φ heat pump and a 7.5 kW supplementary heat strip (Optional Calculation).
    A. 9555   C. 7500
    B. 14,700   D. neither A, B, nor C

_____ **2.** The load is calculated at ___ VA for a dwelling with a 45 A, 240 V, 1φ A/C unit and a 15 kW central heat unit (Optional Calculation).
    A. 10,800   C. 15,000
    B. 20,550   D. 25,800

_____ **3.** The neutral load for general lighting, including required branch circuits, is ___ VA for a 1900 sq ft dwelling.
    A. 5520   C. 7500
    B. 3000   D. 6000

_____ **4.** The CB for protecting a motor feeder that powers a 5 HP, 240 V, 1φ motor and one 3 HP, 240 V, 1φ motors shall not exceed ___ A.
    A. 110   C. 80
    B. 175   D. neither A, B, nor C

_____ **5.** The maximum allowable ampacity for the feeder conductors in Problem 4 is ___ A.
    A. 62   C. 77
    B. 52   D. neither A, B, nor C

_____ **6.** The minimum size XHHW Al ungrounded conductors permitted for a 225 A, 120/240 V, 1φ service for a dwelling is ___.
    A. #4/0   C. 250 kcmil
    B. #3/0   D. 300 kcmil

_____ **7.** A minimum of ___ 15 A general lighting circuits are required for a 2200 sq ft dwelling.
    A. three   C. five
    B. four   D. six

_____ **8.** A 90′ conductor rated at 1.21 Ω/kFT has a total resistance of ___ Ω.
    A. .1089   C. 188.3
    B. 108.9   D. neither A, B, nor C

_____ **9.** A 5760 W A/C load and 10 kW central heat adds ___ VA to the service of a dwelling (Optional Calculation).
    A. 10,000   C. 5760
    B. 6500   D. 15,760

_____ **10.** A 4.5 kW clothes dryer adds ___ A to the neutral load of a dwelling (Standard Calculation).

    A. 18.7   C. 14.6

    B. 13.1   D. 20.8

_____ **11.** A total of ___ KF-2, #10 Cu conductors are permitted to be installed in a ½″ ENT conduit.

    A. six   C. eight

    B. four   D. seven

_____ **12.** The minimum calculated amperage for a 7 kW, 240 V, 1φ household range is ___ A.

    A. 23   C. 58

    B. 29   D. neither A, B, nor C

_____ **13.** The diameter of compact #1 THHN Al is ___″.

    A. .450   C. .508

    B. .415   D. .332

_____ **14.** The allowable fill for a 3″ EMT conduit containing three current-carrying conductors is ___ sq in.

    A. 3.91   C. 3.54

    B. 2.29   D. neither A, B, nor C

_____ **15.** A rating of ___ kW shall be used to calculate the service ungrounded conductor for a dwelling with a 12 kW range (Optional Calculation).

    A. 8   C. 12

    B. 5.6   D. neither A, B, nor C

_____ **16.** A load of ___ kW shall be used to calculate the service grounded conductor for a dwelling with a 12 kW range.

    A. 8   C. 12

    B. 5.6   D. neither A, B, nor C

_____ **17.** The demand factor for services and feeders for five mobile homes shall be ___%.

    A. 100   C. 33

    B. 75   D. 39

_____ **18.** Class 1 power-limited circuits shall be supplied from a source that has a rated output of not more than ___ V.

    A. 50   C. 30

    B. 125   D. 300

_____ **19.** Panelboards equipped with snap switches rated ___ A or less shall have overcurrent protection not in excess of 200 A.

    A. 15   C. 25

    B. 20   D. 30

_____ **20.** Formal interpretation procedures are found in the ___.

    A. NFPA Regulations Governing   C. Code Panel requirements
        Committee Projects

    B. Technical Correlating   D. Underwriters Laboratories specifications
        Committee

Name _____ Date _____

NEC® Examples

A 2 HP, 120 V, 1φ, general duty motor with no code letter is used for Problems 1 through 7.

_____
1. The FLC is ___ A.
   A. 30   C. 24
   B. 17   D. 18.7

_____
2. The minimum size conductors allowed for the branch circuit is #___ THWN Cu.
   A. 12   C. 8
   B. 10   D. 6

_____
3. A ___ A rating is the maximum size overload normally allowed.
   A. 30   C. 36.5
   B. 24   D. 27.6

_____
4. The maximum trip current, if this motor is protected by a thermal device, is ___ A.
   A. 27.6   C. 37.4
   B. 33.6   D. 40.8

_____
5. The maximum ITCB normally allowed is ___ A.
   A. 35   C. 50
   B. 30   D. 60

_____
6. The maximum TDF normally allowed is ___ A.
   A. 45   C. 42
   B. 40   D. 35

_____
7. The maximum one-time fuse normally allowed is ___ A.
   A. 60   C. 75
   B. 70   D. 80

_____
8. Six 13 kW household ranges have a demand load of ___ kW.
   A. 22   C. 31.5
   B. 25   D. 78

_____
9. The minimum size THW Cu conductors required for a 65 A noncontinuous load with 22 current-carrying conductors in a raceway is #___.
   A. 3   C. 2/0
   B. 4   D. 1/0

_____
10. The ampacity of a #6 RHW Al conductor in a raceway with an ambient temperature of 24°C is ___ A.
    A. 50   C. 47
    B. 52.5   D. 60

_____ 11. The resistance of 275′ of #12 THWN Cu stranded conductor is ___ Ω.
        A. 0.56   C. 0.530
        B. 0.5445   D. 0.89

_____ 12. The resistance of a parallel set of 250 kcmil Al conductors in a 175′ installation is ___ Ω.
        A. 14.8   C. 0.0074
        B. 0.1482   D. neither A, B, nor C

_____ 13. Conduit fill allowed for three conductors is ___%.
        A. 55   C. 40
        B. 30   D. 38

_____ 14. The minimum rating of a disconnecting means for a 3 HP, 240 V, 1ϕ motor is ___ A.
        A. 60   C. 30
        B. 40   D. 20

_____ 15. The neutral load for a 14 kW range is ___ VA.
        A. 6160   C. 14,000
        B. 9800   D. neither A, B, nor C

_____ 16. A #6 RHW Cu conductor in a room temperature of 113°F has an ampacity of ___ A.
        A. 53   C. 55
        B. 65   D. neither A, B, nor C

_____ 17. For equipment operating in an ambient temperature of 52°C and drawing 50 A, #___ THHN Cu conductors are required for a 50 A load.
        A. 3   C. 4
        B. 8   D. 6

_____ 18. The general lighting and small appliance and laundry load for a 2500 sq ft dwelling is ___ VA (without applying demand factors).
        A. 5500   C. 7500
        B. 12,000   D. neither A, B, nor C

_____ 19. The branch-circuit load for a 6 kW range is ___ VA.
        A. 4800   C. 8000
        B. 6000   D. neither A, B, nor C

_____ 20. The branch-circuit load for two 4 kW ovens and one 5 kW cooktop unit is ___ VA.
        A. 8000   C. 12,000
        B. 8400   D. 13,000

_____ 21. For a dwelling with a 400 A, 120/240 V, 3-wire, 1ϕ service, ___ kcmil, XHHW Al ungrounded conductors may be permitted.
        A. 800   C. 400
        B. 600   D. neither A, B, nor C

_____ 22. A #___ Cu GEC is required for the service in Problem 21 with a cold water pipe serving as the grounding electrode.
        A. 6   C. 2
        B. 4   D. 1/0

_____ **23.** A conductor with a maximum operating temperature of 167°F in an ambient temperature of 50°C has a correction factor of ___.

    A. .58   C. no correction required

    B. .75   D. neither A, B, nor C

_____ **24.** The maximum amount of #12 THWN-2 conductors that can be installed in a 1″ rigid PVC, Schedule 40 conduit is ___.

    A. 34   C. 25

    B. 15   D. 11

_____ **25.** The percent of derating factor for 42 current-carrying conductors is ___%.

    A. 70   C. 40

    B. 50   D. 35

_____ **26.** The approximate sq in. area of #16 TFFN is ___.

    A. .0072   C. .0109

    B. .0075   D. .0044

_____ **27.** The size of the GEC is based on the ___ conductor.

    A. largest grounded   C. equivalent grounded

    B. largest ungrounded   D. high-leg

_____ **28.** The heating load for a dwelling using electric heat is computed ___ (Standard Calculation).

    A. at 100%   C. per 220.32

    B. at 80%   D. at 125%

_____ **29.** The largest trade size conduit recognized by the NEC® is ___″.

    A. 4   C. 8

    B. 6   D. neither A, B, nor C

_____ **30.** The ampacity of an RHW #10 Cu conductor in free air at 30°C is ___ A.

    A. 55   C. 45

    B. 40   D. 50

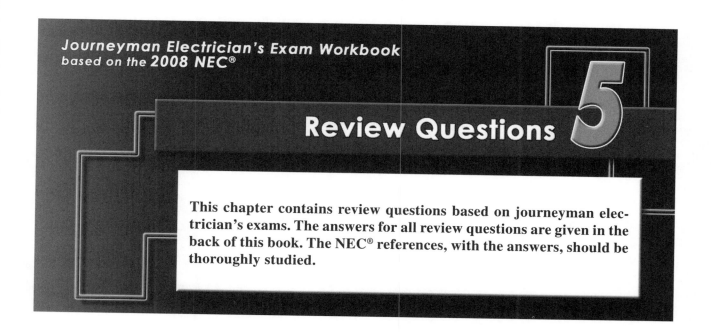

Journeyman Electrician's Exam Workbook
based on the *2008 NEC*®

Review Questions 5

This chapter contains review questions based on journeyman electrician's exams. The answers for all review questions are given in the back of this book. The NEC® references, with the answers, should be thoroughly studied.

REVIEW QUESTIONS

The review questions and problems in this chapter are typical of the questions and problems found on examinations developed by the authority having jurisdiction or a private testing agency. Completing these questions and problems will aid in preparing applicants for the examination.

Note that the questions and problems of each review found in this chapter are sample questions only. In the interest of classroom and study time, these review questions contain less questions than found on a typical journeyman electrician's examination. These review questions are designed as open book tests.

A typical journeyman electrician's examination is based on electrical theory, trade knowledge, NEC® questions, and calculations.

Name _____ Date _____

Time – 45 minutes

_____ **1.** A total of ___ #6 THW Cu conductors are permitted in an 18 cu in. FS box.
    A. zero   C. five
    B. three   D. six

_____ **2.** The stop button is connected in ___ for a motor control circuit.
    A. series   C. series-parallel
    B. parallel   D. jog position

_____ **3.** The nominal phase voltage for a low-voltage wye system is ___ V.
    A. 120   C. 240
    B. 480   D. 208

_____ **4.** The high-leg voltage to ground on a 3ϕ, 4-wire, delta secondary is ___ V.
    A. 208   C. 480
    B. 240   D. 120

_____ **5.** Show windows shall have a receptacle installed for each ___ linear feet.
    A. 10   C. 12
    B. 6   D. 20

_____ **6.** In general, a #___ conductor is the smallest conductor that can be run in parallel.
    A. 1/0   C. 10
    B. 3   D. 8

_____ **7.** One receptacle outlet shall be installed in ___' or longer hallways in a one-family dwelling.
    A. 6   C. 15
    B. 10   D. not required

_____ **8.** A(n) ___ is permitted to be installed on a small appliance circuit.
    A. clock outlet   C. both A and B
    B. refrigerator outlet   D. neither A nor B

_____ **9.** In general, a duplex receptacle in a dwelling shall be based on ___.
    A. 180 VA   C. 1500 W
    B. VA/sq ft   D. the point system

_____ **10.** Show windows are computed on ___ VA per linear foot.
    A. 200   C. 1500
    B. 300   D. 1200

_____ **11.** An ammeter is connected in ___ in a circuit.
  A. parallel   C. series
  B. shunt   D. series-parallel

_____ **12.** ___ or larger determine if a bushing is required on a raceway.
  A. Conduits 1″   C. Conduits 1¼″
  B. Conductors #8   D. Conductors #4

_____ **13.** A ___ is an electrode permitted for grounding.
  A. metal underground water pipe C. plate electrode
  B. ground ring   D. A, B, and C

_____ **14.** The maximum size wire that may be connected under a wire-binding screw with up-turn lugs is #___.
  A. 10   C. 8
  B. 12   D. 14

_____ **15.** A fixture that weighs more than ___ lb shall be supported independently from the box.
  A. 30   C. 60
  B. 50   D. 75

_____ **16.** Motor overloads are sized by the ___.
  A. nameplate   C. motor speed
  B. horsepower   D. duty cycle

_____ **17.** In general the minimum size service for a dwelling is ___ A.
  A. 100   C. 150
  B. 125   D. 60

_____ **18.** One horsepower equals ___ W.
  A. 674   C. 646
  B. 746   D. 476

_____ **19.** The maximum voltage permitted for a pool light is ___ V.
  A. 150   C. 12
  B. 15   D. neither A, B, nor C

_____ **20.** A place of assembly is a building intended for the assembly of ___ or more persons.
  A. 50   C. 150
  B. 100   D. 200

Name _____ Date _____

Time – 45 minutes

_____ 1. If a test lamp lights and burns continuously when placed in series with a capacitor and a suitable source of DC, this is a good indication that the capacitor is ___.
  A. fully charged   C. open
  B. shorted   D. fully discharged

_____ 2. Current is moved through a conductor by ___.
  A. emf   C. ohms
  B. conductance   D. power

_____ 3. Trees shall not be used for ___.
  A. temporary wiring   C. both A and B
  B. support of overhead conductor   D. neither A nor B
    spans

_____ 4. The amperage rating required for a branch-circuit installed to supply an exterior sign shall be a minimum of ___ A.
  A. 15   C. 20
  B. 25   D. neither A, B, nor C

_____ 5. Power is ___ voltage times current, in a pure resistive circuit.
  A. double the   C. AC
  B. always   D. never

_____ 6. ___ lighting is a string of outdoor lights suspended between two points.
  A. Mood   C. Malibu
  B. Party   D. neither A, B, nor C

_____ 7. Wound-rotor and squirrel-cage motors are two types of ___ motors.
  A. universal   C. induction
  B. synchronous   D. single-phase

_____ 8. A(n) ___ motor can operate on AC or DC.
  A. torque   C. capacitor-start
  B. induction   D. universal

_____ 9. A good lubricant for pulling wire is ___.
  A. motor oil   C. grease
  B. kerosene   D. neither A, B, nor C

_____ 10. Voltaic reaction is ___.
  A. chemical   C. both A and B
  B. fission   D. neither A nor B

_____ **11.** Insulating safety hand grips on tools ___.

      A. are not enough to prevent   C. should be used with other insulating
          electrical shock   equipment
      B. are not meant to prevent   D. all of the above
          electrical shock

_____ **12.** A ___ is two dissimilar metals joined together.

      A. Joule   C. thermocouple
      B. Coulomb   D. phase union

_____ **13.** A(n) ___ is used to measure the speed of an armature directly in rpm.

      A. tachometer   C. ohmmeter
      B. megger   D. chronometer

_____ **14.** A(n) ___ motor has a wide speed range.

      A. DC   C. synchronous
      B. AC   D. induction

_____ **15.** The ___ winding of a current transformer carries the most current.

      A. primary   C. interwinding
      B. secondary   D. coil

_____ **16.** The best electrical conductor (of those listed) is ___.

      A. copper   C. silver
      B. gold   D. aluminum

_____ **17.** Ambient temperature is the ___.

      A. temperature of the wire   C. temperature of the area surrounding the wire
      B. differential temperature   D. melting temperature of the insulation

_____ **18.** A western union splice is for ___.

      A. underground use only   C. strengthening a splice
      B. the utility companies use only   D. neither A, B, nor C

_____ **19.** ___ breaks down rubber insulation.

      A. Grease   C. Acid
      B. Water   D. neither A, B, nor C

_____ **20.** The 120 V windings of a 120/240 V, 1ϕ motor are connected in ___ when connected
      to a 120 V supply.

      A. series   C. series-parallel
      B. parallel   D. neither A, B, nor C

Name _____ Date _____

Time – 45 minutes

_____ 1. A(n) ___ conductor has the highest temperature rating (of those listed).
   A. RH   C. THHN
   B. RHW   D. TW

_____ 2. The wiring method approved for installation in ducts which transport dust is ___.
   A. rigid metal conduit   C. IMC
   B. EMT   D. neither A, B, nor C

_____ 3. ___ is the best metal for magnets (of those listed).
   A. Brass   C. Zinc
   B. Steel   D. Tin

_____ 4. Electrical equipment secured to and in contact with a metal rack or structure provided for its support shall be ___.
   A. secured   C. bonded
   B. effectively grounded D. effectively attached

_____ 5. All metal parts within ___′ horizontally of the inside walls of a pool shall be bonded together.
   A. 20   C. 10
   B. 15   D. 5

_____ 6. Each cell shall be computed at ___ V in a stationary alkali storage battery.
   A. 1.5   C. 1.2
   B. 2   D. 3

_____ 7. ___ are not covered under the NEC®.
   A. Marinas   C. Coal mines
   B. Aircraft hangers   D. Utility company offices

_____ 8. The demand factor for a feeder supplying 23 recreational vehicle sites is ___%.
   A. 53   C. 45
   B. 43   D. 42

_____ 9. The smallest TC Cu cable permitted is #___.
   A. 14   C. 3
   B. 12   D. 18

_____ 10. The minimum branch circuit rating shall be ___ A for an 8¾ kW household range.
   A. 40   C. 30
   B. 35   D. 50

_____ 11. Overhead conductors for outdoor lighting shall not be smaller than #___ Cu for spans longer than 50'.
    A. 14   C. 10
    B. 12   D. 8

_____ 12. A 277 V lighting fixture used for outdoor illumination on an office building shall be installed not less than ___' from a window.
    A. 3   C. 6
    B. 4   D. 5

_____ 13. There shall be no more than ___ disconnect(s) per service grouped in any one location.
    A. one   C. four
    B. three   D. six

_____ 14. The ampacity of #12 UF wire is ___ A.
    A. 25   C. 15
    B. 20   D. 30

_____ 15. ___ is a grounding electrode.
    A. Cold water pipe   C. Ground plate
    B. Ground ring   D. A, B, and C

_____ 16. ___ wire is used for switchboards only.
    A. TFE   C. SIS
    B. THWN   D. SA

_____ 17. The ampacity of #8 Romex is ___ A.
    A. 35   C. 50
    B. 40   D. 55

_____ 18. A temperature of 86°F is ___ 30°C.
    A. the same as   C. 32°F more than
    B. 32°F less than   D. neither A, B, nor C

_____ 19. If the neutral of a 120/240 V, 1φ, 3-wire branch circuit opens, the source voltage is ___ V.
    A. 120   C. 240
    B. 208   D. neither A, B, nor C

_____ 20. In a 120/240 V, 1φ, 3-wire branch circuit, if Line A draws 5 A and Line B draws 10 A, ___ A is drawn on the neutral.
    A. 0   C. 10
    B. 5   D. 15

Name _____ Date _____

Time – 45 minutes

_____ **1.** Conduits through which moisture may contact energized parts shall be ___ at either or both ends.

    A. open   C. sealed

    B. arranged to drain   D. threaded

_____ **2.** The minimum size conductor permitted to be installed in cablebus is ___.

    A. #3   C. 250 kcmil

    B. #1/0   D. #4/0

_____ **3.** The ampacity of the line conductors from a generator to the first OCPD shall be not less than ___% of the nameplate current information on the generator.

    A. 110   C. 125

    B. 115   D. 300

_____ **4.** When charging a battery, ___ is given off.

    A. carbon dioxide   C. helium

    B. hydrogen   D. mercury

_____ **5.** Voltage generated by the compression of certain crystals is ___.

    A. hysteresis   C. mercury vapor

    B. thermionic emission   D. piezoelectric effect

_____ **6.** The effective value of AC voltage is ___.

    A. .707 × maximum value   C. both A and B

    B. the RMS value   D. neither A, B, nor C

_____ **7.** The high leg of a delta secondary shall be connected to ___.

    A. Phase A   C. Phase C

    B. Phase B   D. the neutral bar

_____ **8.** Drywall surfaces that are damaged must be repaired so there will be no open spaces greater than ___″ at the edge of the box.

    A. ⅛   C. ³⁄₁₆

    B. ¼   D. ⅜

_____ **9.** Metal wireways containing more than ___ current-carrying conductors at any cross section shall be derated.

    A. 20   C. 40

    B. 30   D. 35

_____ 10. The circuit of a control system that handles the electric signals directing the control of a controller, but does not carry the main power current, is a ___ circuit.

    A. signaling   C. motor control

    B. remote-control   D. power-limited

_____ 11. Edison-base plug fuses shall be classified at not more than ___ V, and 30 A and less.

    A. 125   C. 300

    B. 150   D. 130

_____ 12. Wire bending space at terminals in meter sockets is ___.

    A. covered in the NEC®   C. covered by public service commission

    B. utility controlled   D. a state standard

_____ 13. FPN stands for ___.

    A. fire protection note   C. fire panel notation

    B. fine print note   D. neither A, B, nor C

_____ 14. The fluorescent ballast with the quietest noise rating is Type ___.

    A. Q   C. A

    B. F   D. Q/S

_____ 15. A receptacle in a commercial bathroom shall be ___.

    A. orange   C. GFCI-protected

    B. within 6′ of the sink   D. a minimum wire size of #12 Cu

_____ 16. The maximum distance between receptacles over a kitchen countertop is ___.

    A. 2′   C. 6′

    B. 12″   D. 4′

_____ 17. Floor receptacles installed in a living room shall not be counted as part of the required outlets unless located ___ the wall.

    A. close to   C. within 18″ of

    B. within 20″ of   D. within 2′ of

_____ 18. A 6′ section of track lighting in a dwelling would increase the branch load ___.

    A. 0 W   C. 450 W

    B. 1.5 A per ft   D. 6 A

_____ 19. The ampacity of #16 TF Cu conductor is ___ A.

    A. 15   C. 8

    B. 6   D. 4

_____ 20. Where practical, dissimilar metals in contact anywhere in the system using rigid metal conduit shall be avoided to eliminate the possibility of ___.

    A. hysteresis   C. inductive action

    B. galvanic action   D. coefficient effect

Name _____ Date _____

Time – 45 minutes

_____ 1. The minimum clearance for overhead service conductors above a public driveway is ___′.
    A. 15   C. 12
    B. 18   D. 10

_____ 2. The minimum clearance for service conductors over residential driveways not subject to truck traffic is ___′.
    A. 10   C. 15
    B. 12   D. 18

_____ 3. Dry-type transformers located indoors and rated 112.5 kVA or less shall be at least ___″ from combustible material.
    A. 12   C. 24
    B. 18   D. 15

_____ 4. Type NM cable must clear a scuttle hole by ___′.
    A. 0   C. 6
    B. 2   D. 5

_____ 5. When a storage battery loses its charge and must be recharged, the recharging current must come from a(n) ___ source.
    A. AC   C. full power
    B. DC   D. transformer

_____ 6. The high-leg voltage on a delta secondary is ___ V.
    A. 208   C. 240
    B. 277   D. 120

_____ 7. The largest size EMT permitted is ___″.
    A. 4   C. 5
    B. 6   D. 8

_____ 8. Branch-circuit conductors for fixed-resistance space heaters shall be rated at ___%.
    A. 250   C. 300
    B. 80   D. 125

_____ 9. A ___ in a dwelling unit shall be supplied by the two 20 A small-appliance circuits.
    A. kitchen   C. dining room
    B. pantry   D. A, B, and C

_____ **10.** The minimum burial depth for PVC conduit under a 4″ concrete slab is ___″.

A. 24   C. 4

B. 18   D. 0

_____ **11.** ___ may be connected ahead of the service disconnects.

A. Nothing   C. Service fuses

B. Surge arresters   D. both B and C

_____ **12.** All splices, joints, and the free ends of conductors are required to be covered with an insulation ___ the conductor.

A. as thick as   C. thicker than

B. twice the size of   D. half as thick as

_____ **13.** Where an AC system operating at less than ___ V is grounded at any point, the grounded conductor must be run to each service.

A. 1000   C. 600

B. 300   D. 1500

_____ **14.** Raceways enclosing service-entrance conductors shall be suitable for ___ locations, and arranged to drain where exposed to the weather.

A. wet   C. weatherproof

B. watertight   D. sealed

_____ **15.** AWG #1/0 Cu conductors in a vertical raceway shall be supported at intervals not exceeding ___′.

A. 50   C. 100

B. 75   D. 125

_____ **16.** In a dwelling all 15A and 25A branch circuits in a bedroom must be protected by a(n) ___.

A. circuit breaker   C. arc-fault circuit interrupter

B. GFIC protector   D. surge circuit protector

_____ **17.** In areas where walls are frequently washed, conduit and boxes shall be ___.

A. mounted on ¼″ spacers   C. dipped in rustproofing material

B. mounted at least 8′ from floor   D. PVC only

_____ **18.** A receptacle to serve a countertop in a dining room of a dwelling unit shall be located not more than ___″ above the unit.

A. 20   C. 12

B. 6   D. as per plans

_____ **19.** The maximum length for a cord supplying a 240 V room air conditioner is ___′.

A. 6   C. 3

B. 10   D. 5

_____ **20.** A ___ is permitted for connecting the GEC.

A. plumbing strap   C. both A and B

B. pipe plug   D. neither A nor B

Name _____ Date _____

Time – 45 minutes

_____ **1.** A storage battery for emergency lighting and power shall maintain not less than 87½% of the total voltage at the total load for a period of at least ___.
   A. 2 hrs   C. 1 hr
   B. 1½ hrs   D. 30 minutes

_____ **2.** On circuits of 600 V or less, overhead spans up to 50′ shall have Cu conductors not smaller than #___.
   A. 12   C. 8
   B. 10   D. 6

_____ **3.** ___ may be installed in a raceway containing service entrance conductors.
   A. Grounding conductors   C. either A or B
   B. Bonding jumpers   D. neither A nor B

_____ **4.** The ampacity for AC transformer welders is determined by ___.
   A. rating plate and duty cycle   C. secondary current
   B. kVA and nameplate   D. neither A, B, nor C

_____ **5.** The minimum size conductor required for an arc projector is #___.
   A. 10   C. 6
   B. 8   D. 4

_____ **6.** "DANGER HIGH VOLTAGE KEEP OUT" must be posted when voltage exceeds ___V.
   A. 277   C. 600
   B. 480   D. 1000

_____ **7.** Overcurrent devices shall be enclosed in ___.
   A. cabinets   C. both A and B
   B. cutout boxes   D. neither A nor B

_____ **8.** The main bonding jumper shall be a ___.
   A. bus   C. both A and B
   B. screw   D. neither A nor B

_____ **9.** Wooden plugs driven into holes in masonry are permitted to support boxes weighing no more than ___ lb.
   A. 6   C. 50
   B. 10   D. neither A, B, nor C

_____ **10.** The center of the handle of CBs used as switches shall be installed no higher than ___ above the floor or working platform.
    A. 6'-7"   C. 8'
    B. 6'   D. shall be readily accessible

_____ **11.** SE Cable can be used for branch circuits where the ungrounded conductors are ___ covered type.
    A. nylon   C. ethylene
    B. silicone   D. thermoplastic

_____ **12.** The minimum bending space for one 250 kcmil conductor in a gutter is ___".
    A. 4½   C. 6
    B. 5   D. 10

_____ **13.** AWG #___ service conductors are required for a 100 A, 120/240 V, 1ϕ service for a dwelling unit.
    A. 3 THW Cu   C. 4 THW Cu
    B. 2 TW Al   D. 4 XHHW Al

_____ **14.** When service entrance conductors exceed 1100 MCM for copper, the bonding jumper shall be at least ___% of the largest phase conductor.
    A. 15   C. 12½
    B. 10   D. 8

_____ **15.** Transformers used to step-up voltage for general use are classified as ___ systems.
    A. separately derived   C. UPS
    B. emergency   D. standby

_____ **16.** ___ is covered in the NEC®.
    A. Electric utility service drop   C. Power generation plant
    B. Electric utility office building D. Electric utility substation

_____ **17.** Nonmetallic extensions shall be secured in place at intervals not exceeding ___".
    A. 6   C. 10
    B. 8   D. 16

_____ **18.** Service cables mounted in contact with a building shall be supported at intervals not exceeding ___".
    A. 10   C. 15
    B. 24   D. 30

_____ **19.** A starting switch in a motor control circuit is wired in ___ with the holding contacts.
    A. series   C. series-parallel
    B. parallel   D. neither A, B, nor C

_____ **20.** Solenoids are ___ magnets.
    A. permanent   C. electro
    B. natural   D. neither A, B, nor C

Name _____ Date _____

Time – 45 minutes

_____ **1.** Fault current is ___.
    A. locked rotor amps   C. metric amps
    B. internal battery current   D. neither A, B, nor C

_____ **2.** If the voltage measures 208 V between phase conductors in a 3ϕ system, ___ V is the measurement to the neutral.
    A. 277   C. 208
    B. 120   D. 230

_____ **3.** Ions, electrolyte, and amp hours pertain to ___.
    A. condensers   C. batteries
    B. ballast   D. transformers

_____ **4.** In a 3ϕ distribution system, the phase voltages are ___° apart.
    A. 120   C. 90
    B. 360   D. 60

_____ **5.** Two wattmeters are required to measure power on a ___ system.
    A. 1ϕ   C. complex
    B. 3ϕ   D. demand

_____ **6.** The minimum burial depth for a 20 A, 120 V, GFCI-protected residential branch circuit, using UF wire, is ___″.
    A. 12   C. 24
    B. 18   D. 6

_____ **7.** The EGC is sized by the ___.
    A. conduit diameter   C. overcurrent device rating
    B. ungrounded conductors   D. disconnect

_____ **8.** Impedance is ___.
    A. inductive reactance   C. total resistance in a DC circuit
    B. capacitive reactance   D. total resistance in an AC circuit

_____ **9.** A ___ is used for testing specific gravity.
    A. megger   C. hydrometer
    B. galvometer   D. tachometer

_____ **10.** The thickness of insulation for SIS #8 wire is ___ mil.
    A. 45   C. 60
    B. 50   D. 75

_____ 11. Hanging electrical fixtures located directly above any part of the bathtub shall be installed so that the fixture is not less than ___′ above the top of the bathtub.

    A. 8   C. 7

    B. 6   D. neither A, B, nor C

_____ 12. Angle pull dimensional requirements apply to junction boxes only when the size of the conductor is equal to or larger than #___.

    A. 0   C. 3/0

    B. 4   D. 6

_____ 13. Metal enclosures for GECs shall be ___.

    A. rigid conduit only   C. electrically continuous

    B. watertight   D. raintight

_____ 14. Aluminum grounding conductors used outside shall not be installed within ___″ of earth.

    A. 18   C. 12

    B. 24   D. aluminum not permitted

_____ 15. Service conductors run above the top level of a window shall be ___.

    A. 3′ above window   C. 8′ above window

    B. considered out-of-reach   D. accessible

_____ 16. The minimum size GEC is #___.

    A. 6   C. 8

    B. 10   D. 4

_____ 17. ___ is not permitted to be installed above a drop ceiling used as a return air system.

    A. IMC   C. RMC

    B. EMT   D. NMC

_____ 18. Nail plates are required to be at least ___″ thick.

    A. $\frac{1}{16}$ C. $\frac{1}{4}$

    B. $\frac{1}{8}$ D. $\frac{3}{16}$

_____ 19. The color ___ is to be used for marking the high leg.

    A. white   C. gray

    B. red   D. orange

_____ 20. ___ are used to fasten an enclosure to a hollow-block wall.

    A. Wood plugs   C. Concrete anchors

    B. Toggle bolts   D. Lag bolts

Name _____ Date _____

Time – 45 minutes

_____ 1. The highest amperage at the rated voltage that an OCPD is intended to open under standard test conditions is its ___ rating.
    A. ampacity   C. load
    B. interrupting   D. maximum

_____ 2. A DC voltmeter may also be used to measure ___.
    A. henrys   C. ohms
    B. inductance   D. frequency

_____ 3. One advantage of 240 V over 120 V, based on the same wattage, is ___.
    A. less voltage drop   C. less power
    B. more power   D. neither A, B, nor C

_____ 4. The current leads the voltage when ___.
    A. reactance exceeds inductance   C. resistance exceeds capacitance
    B. inductive reactance exceeds   D. capacitive reactance exceeds capacitive
       reactance   inductive reactance

_____ 5. Heating the junction of two dissimilar alloys causes ___.
    A. electrons to flow   C. inductance
    B. arcing   D. fission

_____ 6. Incandescent lamps are filled with ___.
    A. neon   C. nitrogen
    B. hydrogen   D. dry air

_____ 7. A lamp can be controlled from three different points by ___ switches.
    A. two 3-way and one 4-way   C. two 3-ways and one DP
    B. three 3-way   D. two DP and one SP

_____ 8. A(n) ___ is an instrument for measuring the flow of electrons.
    A. ohmmeter   C. ammeter
    B. voltmeter   D. wattmeter

_____ 9. A battery operates on the principle of ___ energy.
    A. magnetic   C. static
    B. heat   D. chemical

_____ 10. ___ conductors shall be used for wiring on fixture chains.
    A. Solid   C. Wrapped
    B. Covered   D. Stranded

_____ **11.** A blue lead in a heating cable indicates it is for ___ V.

      A. 120   C. 240

      B. 208   D. 277

_____ **12.** The largest standard ITCB is ___ A.

      A. 4000   C. 6000

      B. 3000   D. 8000

_____ **13.** Hysteresis, eddy currents, and ampere turns are terms used when referring to ___.

      A. motors   C. generators

      B. lightning arresters   D. transformers

_____ **14.** One receptacle installed on an individual branch circuit shall have a rating not less than ___% of the rating of the branch circuit.

      A. 50   C. 100

      B. 80   D. 125

_____ **15.** A ___ A OCPD is required for a 7.5 kW, 240 V, 1φ strip heater.

      A. 35   C. 40

      B. 60   D. 39

_____ **16.** The maximum resistance to ground for a supplemental electrode is ___ Ω.

      A. infinity   C. 100

      B. 25   D. 50

_____ **17.** Piezo electricity is caused by ___ applied to crystals.

      A. chemicals   C. pressure

      B. light   D. heat

_____ **18.** The approximate diameter of #12 THW is ___".

      A. 0.212   C. 0.182

      B. 0.13   D. 0.152

_____ **19.** Because aluminum is not magnetic, there is no heating due to ___.

      A. electrolysis   C. capacitance

      B. hysteresis   D. impedance

_____ **20.** Rigid metal conduit must be buried at least ___" in locations not otherwise specified.

      A. 6   C. 18

      B. 12   D. 24

Name _____ Date _____

Time – 45 minutes

_____ **1.** ___ is the opposition to the flow of magnetic flux.
  A. Henrys   C. Reluctance
  B. Inductance   D. Mhos

_____ **2.** A three-conductor cord for a kitchen disposal shall be not less than ___″ nor more than ___″ in length.
  A. 18;36   C. 16;30
  B. 18;48   D. 16;36

_____ **3.** The ampacity of a capacitor's circuit conductors shall not be less than ___% of the rated amperage of the capacitor.
  A. 110   C. 125
  B. 115   D. 135

_____ **4.** If the voltage of a circuit is constant, the amperage ___ when the resistance is increased.
  A. decreases   C. increases
  B. remains the same   D. drops to zero

_____ **5.** Conductors supplying an outlet for a professional-type xenon projector shall not be smaller than #___.
  A. 8   C. 4
  B. 6   D. 3

_____ **6.** Conductors of #___ and larger size shall be stranded when installed in conduit.
  A. 6   C. 8
  B. 4   D. 10

_____ **7.** A(n) ___ is used to convert AC into DC.
  A. condenser   C. electromagnet
  B. rectifier   D. transformer

_____ **8.** The ___ is the unit of measurement for capacitance.
  A. Henry   C. Farad
  B. Ohm   D. Var

_____ **9.** The ___ is the unit of measurement for capacitive reactance.
  A. Henry   C. Farad
  B. Ohm   D. Var

_____ **10.** Electric discharge lighting with exposed live parts having an open-circuit voltage exceeding ___ V shall not be installed in dwelling units.
  A. 125   C. 300
  B. 150   D. neither A, B, nor C

_____ **11.** NFPA regulations governing committee projects is concerned with ___.
  A. the Standards Council for the NFPA   C. Code Panel selection
  B. formal Code interpretation procedures D. Code Panel No. 20 only

_____ **12.** Conductors within ___″ of a ballast compartment shall have an insulation rating not lower than 90°C.
  A. 3   C. 5
  B. 4   D. not permitted

_____ **13.** A Wheatstone Bridge is used to measure ___.
  A. inductance   C. reluctance
  B. conductance   D. medium and high resistance

_____ **14.** A dynamo is ___.
  A. an electromagnet   C. a solid state transformer
  B. used to convert mechanical D. a rectifier
     energy into electrical energy

_____ **15.** If batteries are connected in series, the voltage ___.
  A. increases   C. is unchanged
  B. decreases   D. drops to zero

_____ **16.** A fixed appliance is ___.
  A. not easily moved from one place to another   C. both A and B
  B. fastened or otherwise secured at   D. neither A nor B
     a specific location

_____ **17.** The NEC® contains provisions considered necessary for ___.
  A. efficiency   C. convenience
  B. future expansion   D. safety

_____ **18.** The most heat is created when AC passes through a 10 Ω ___.
  A. condenser   C. resistor
  B. inductive coil   D. heat is equal for A, B, and C

_____ **19.** The demand factor for 45 household electric clothes dryers is ___%.
  A. 100   C. 32.5
  B. 90   D. 25

_____ **20.** In general, the grounded conductor shall not be ___.
  A. covered   C. bare
  B. fused   D. the color white

Name _____ Date _____

Time – 45 minutes

_____ **1.** A Type S fuse adapter rated at 30 A will accommodate a ___ A fuse.
   A. 20   C. 35
   B. 25   D. either A, B, or C

_____ **2.** True power is always volts times amps ___.
   A. in an AC circuit   C. where the frequency is constant
   B. in a DC circuit   D. neither A, B, nor C

_____ **3.** The general lighting load for a lodge room shall be based on ___.
   A. the number of lighting units   C. 1½ VA/sq ft
   B. the lumen output   D. the ballast ratings and lamp sizes

_____ **4.** ___ copper is used for all covered or insulated copper conductors.
   A. Soft-drawn   C. Medium hard-drawn
   B. Hard-drawn   D. neither A, B, nor C

_____ **5.** ___ shall not be used on RMC for connection at couplings.
   A. Running threads   C. Unions
   B. Aluminum fittings   D. either A, B, or C

_____ **6.** Class II locations are hazardous because of the presence of ___.
   A. easily ignitable fibers   C. combustible dust
   B. flammable gases   D. flammable vapors

_____ **7.** The frames of household ranges and clothes dryers are permitted to be grounded to the grounded conductor for ___.
   A. existing installations   C. mobile homes
   B. recreational vehicles   D. either A, B, or C

_____ **8.** Volume deductions for combinations of conductor sizes in a box shall be based on ___.
   A. insulation type   C. Table 314.16(A)
   B. Table 314.16(B)   D. Ch. 9 Table 4

_____ **9.** The phase-to-neutral voltage of a 3φ, 4-wire, 480 V, wye-connected secondary is ___ V.
   A. 208   C. 240
   B. 120   D. 277

_____ **10.** Three-way and four-way switches shall be wired so that all switching occurs only in the ___ circuit conductor.

    A. ungrounded   C. neutral

    B. grounded   D. neither A, B, nor C

_____ **11.** An autotransformer has ___.

    A. one winding   C. three windings

    B. two windings   D. an rotor

_____ **12.** AC/DC general-use snap switches are allowed for inductive loads not exceeding ___% of the current rating of the switch at the applied voltage.

    A. 50   C. 125

    B. 80   D. 200

_____ **13.** The minimum cover for PVC under a building is ___″.

    A. 6   C. 12

    B. 18   D. 0

_____ **14.** The unit of measurement for inductance is ___.

    A. Ohms   C. Henry

    B. Mhos   D. Farad

_____ **15.** A ___ is used to measure specific gravity.

    A. galvanometer   C. multimeter

    B. hydrometer   D. VM

_____ **16.** The ampacity of a #8 bare conductor installed with two insulated #8 THW Cu conductors in the same raceway is ___ A.

    A. 40   C. 50

    B. 70   D. 55

_____ **17.** Transformer output is rated in ___.

    A. Henrys   C. kVA

    B. Ohms   D. kW

_____ **18.** The combination of two dissimilar metals is a ___.

    A. battery action   C. piezo effect

    B. thermocouple   D. photo cell action

_____ **19.** The EGC of conductors run in parallel shall be sized per ___.

    A. 250.94   C. Table 310.16

    B. 250.122   D. 240.3

_____ **20.** A branch-circuit supplying a 120 gal. fixed storage water heater shall have a rating not less than ___% of the nameplate rating.

    A. 80   C. 125

    B. 50   D. 150

Name _____ Date _____

Time – 45 minutes

_____ 1. EMT couplings and connectors used in masonry shall be ___.
   A. concretetight   C. weatherproof
   B. watertight   D. die cast metal

_____ 2. Where ___ cable terminates, an approved seal shall be provided immediately after stripping to prevent the entrance of moisture into the insulation.
   A. TC   C. SE
   B. MI   D. MC

_____ 3. A(n) ___ is a protective device for limiting surge voltages by discharging surge amperage.
   A. GFCI CB   C. current-limiting fuse
   B. ITCB   D. surge arrester

_____ 4. The allowable ampacity for each conductor of six current-carrying conductors shall be reduced to ___%.
   A. 80   C. 70
   B. 160   D. 125

_____ 5. A total of ___ #12 conductors is allowed in a 4″ × 1¼″ square box.
   A. ten   C. eight
   B. nine   D. twelve

_____ 6. A(n) ___ is not required to be grounded.
   A. electrolytic cell   C. portable hand lamp
   B. aquarium   D. snow blower

_____ 7. A pool light operating at more than ___ V requires GFCI protection.
   A. 12   C. 14
   B. 13   D. 15

_____ 8. The maximum number of #12 TFN conductors permitted for a ⅜″ flexible metal conduit with outside fittings is ___.
   A. three   C. five
   B. four   D. six

_____ 9. Multiwire branch-circuits shall supply only ___ loads.
   A. line-to-neutral   C. line-to-ground
   B. line-to-phase   D. phase-to-phase

_____ **10.** ___ electrons are electrons that are easily moved.
     A. Orbiting   C. Free
     B. Ring   D. Loose

_____ **11.** Portions of an interior raceway system exposed to widely different temperatures shall be ___.
     A. coated   C. filled with an approved material
     B. isolated   D. corrected for temperature

_____ **12.** Electromotive force can be raised or lowered by using a ___.
     A. rectifier   C. capacitor
     B. transformer   D. magnet

_____ **13.** A totally enclosed switchboard shall have a space of not less than ___′ from the ceiling.
     A. 6   C. 3
     B. 8   D. 4

_____ **14.** ___ should not be covered.
     A. J-boxes   C. Panel boxes
     B. Conduit bodies   D. Switchboards

_____ **15.** Short radius elbows containing #___ conductors or smaller shall not contain splices.
     A. 3   C. 6
     B. 1/0   D. 4

_____ **16.** Each ___′, or fraction thereof, of a fixed multioutlet assembly used in lighting a store show room shall be considered as an outlet of not less than 180 VA.
     A. 5   C. 2
     B. 1   D. 4

_____ **17.** Conductors are considered outside of a building where covered by ___″ of concrete beneath the building.
     A. 6   C. 3
     B. 4   D. 2

_____ **18.** Junction boxes shall be ___.
     A. accessible   C. exposed
     B. readily accessible D. either A, B, or C

_____ **19.** General lighting receptacles in a dwelling are based on ___.
     A. a point system   C. 180 VA
     B. amps per outlet   D. watts per sq ft

_____ **20.** ___ shall not be connected to the supply side of a service disconnect.
     A. Surge protection C. Cable limiters
     B. Meters   D. Secondary ties

Name _____ Date _____

Time – 45 minutes

_____ **1.** Two or more ground rods shall be not less than ___′ apart.
  A. 2   C. 5
  B. 4   D. 6

_____ **2.** In a vertical raceway, #2/0 Al conductors shall be supported at intervals not exceeding ___′.
  A. 100   C. 180
  B. 200   D. 80

_____ **3.** RNC shall not be installed in an ambient temperature exceeding ___°F.
  A. 122   C. 140
  B. 167   D. 190

_____ **4.** The allowable percentage of tubing fill for two RHW Cu conductors is ___%.
  A. 100   C. 80
  B. 40   D. 31

_____ **5.** Supplementary overcurrent protection shall ___.
  A. be a substitute for branch circuit OCPD   C. be readily accessible
  B. be sized smaller than branch   D. not be used as a substitute for
     circuit OCPD   branch circuit OCPD

_____ **6.** A fluorescent fixture installed in a clothes closet shall have a minimum of ___″ clearance between the fixture and the nearest point of storage.
  A. 12   C. 18
  B. 6   D. 24

_____ **7.** The length of the cord for a cord-and-plug connected trash compactor shall not exceed ___′.
  A. 3   C. 5
  B. 4   D. 6

_____ **8.** An A/C unit has a load of 7200 VA. The central electric heat is rated at 15 kVA. A total of ___ VA is added to the service load calculation.
  A. 15,000   C. 14,430
  B. 9750   D. neither A, B, nor C

_____ **9.** In general, the maximum overcurrent protection for #6 THWN Cu is ___ A.
  A. 60   C. 70
  B. 65   D. 66

_____ 10. The bonding conductor for a swimming pool shall not be smaller than #8 solid Cu, which is ___.
    A. insulated   C. bare
    B. covered   D. either A, B, or C

_____ 11. Four light bulbs in a single fixture should be ___-connected.
    A. series   C. parallel
    B. wye   D. series-parallel

_____ 12. To reverse the rotation of a 3ϕ motor, ___.
    A. reverse all leads   C. reverse armature leads
    B. reverse capacitor leads   D. reverse any two line leads

_____ 13. Each commercial receptacle shall be counted as ___ VA.
    A. 120   C. 180
    B. 300   D. 1500

_____ 14. The demand factor for three electric ranges in a restaurant is ___%.
    A. 60   C. 80
    B. 70   D. 90

_____ 15. Flexible cord shall not be used as a substitute for ___ wiring.
    A. temporary   C. concealed
    B. fixed   D. neither A, B, nor C

_____ 16. An alternation is ___.
    A. 360°   C. one hertz
    B. one cycle   D. ½ cycle

_____ 17. Specifications for plans ___.
    A. set minimum standards   C. set job schedules
    B. provide work divisions   D. are part of the contract

_____ 18. The number 32 in a 6-32 machine screw refers to the ___.
    A. screw size   C. threads per inch
    B. screw pitch   D. screw diameter

_____ 19. Smaller gauges of wire are pencil stripped to prevent ___.
    A. cutting the wire   C. nicks in the wire
    B. damage to insulation   D. A, B, or C

_____ 20. The vector sum of the phase currents is equal to ___ in a balanced, resistive 3ϕ system.
    A. zero   C. 1.73 × Phase A
    B. Phase A × PF   D. 3 × Phase A

Name _____ Date _____

Time – 45 minutes

_____ 1. A building's service ungrounded conductors are 500 kcmil Cu and its GES is a metal water pipe. A ___ Cu GEC is required.
   A. #3/0   C. 500 kcmil
   B. #2   D. #1/0

_____ 2. An AC transformer arc welder has a nameplate primary current of 90 A at 240 V with a 30% duty cycle. The supply conductors shall be ___ A.
   A. 50   C. 117
   B. 90   D. 105

_____ 3. A device box contains two #14 conductors, three #12 conductors, one EGC, one duplex receptacle, and two cable clamps. A(n) ___ cu in. device box is required.
   A. 21   C. 18
   B. 19.75   D. 25.5

_____ 4. A device box contains four #12 conductors and two EGCs. A fixture to be mounted to the box has four #16 conductors. A(n) ___ cu in. device box is required.
   A. 18.25   C. 18
   B. 15.5   D. 11.25

_____ 5. Five #10 THWN Cu current-carrying conductors are installed in a raceway with an ambient temperature of 32°C. The #10 conductors shall be ___ A.
   A. 24   C. 26.3
   B. 22.5   D. 28

_____ 6. A 120/240 V, 1ϕ, 3-wire system has two 1.5 kVA, 120 V, 1ϕ resistive loads, one 2 HP, 230 V, 1ϕ motor, and three 1 HP, 120 V, 1ϕ motors. The current on the neutral is ___ A. (All loads are balanced as close as possible.)
   A. 16   C. 32
   B. 12.5   D. neither A, B, nor C

_____ 7. A ⅜″ flexible metal conduit with two ungrounded #12 XHHW conductors and one bare #12 EGC requires a ___.
   A. fitting inside   C. fitting not permitted
   B. fitting outside   D. neither A, B, nor C

_____ 8. A transformer arc welder with a primary current of 40 A and a 60% duty-cycle has a ___ A FLC.
   A. 24   C. 31
   B. 40   D. 50

_____ **9.** The maximum OCPD for the arc welder in Problem 8 is ___ A.
        A. 40   C. 75
        B. 50   D. 80

_____ **10.** A capacitor has a rated current of 18 A. The required ampacity for the circuit conductors is ___ A.
        A. 18   C. 54
        B. 22.5   D. 24.3

_____ **11.** SJOO cord rated at 300 V is manufactured in AWG sizes ___.
        A. 18–10   C. 14–6
        B. 16–8   D. 16–12

_____ **12.** In general, the branch-circuit selection current for a hermetic refrigerant motor-compressor shall be based on ___.
        A. NEC® tables   C. calculations as per Article 430
        B. the equipment nameplate   D. the compressor overload rating

_____ **13.** Branch circuits that supply neon signs shall not be rated in excess of ___ A.
        A. 40   C. 60
        B. 50   D. 30

_____ **14.** Definitions that apply regarding the NEC® rules for communications systems include ___.
        A. block   C. wire
        B. cable   D. all of the above

_____ **15.** In a circuit, switches or circuit breakers shall not disconnect the ___ conductor.
        A. ungrounded   C. grounded
        B. phase   D. high leg

_____ **16.** The definition for *electrical datum plane* is found in NEC® Article ___.
        A. 810   C. 430
        B. 555   D. 500

_____ **17.** Heavy-duty track lighting is identified for uses exceeding ___ A.
        A. 15   C. 12
        B. 20   D. 16

_____ **18.** The minimum bending radius for 2″ Type IGS cable is ___″.
        A. 24   C. 16
        B. 20   D. 18

_____ **19.** Constant wattage heating cables shall not exceed ___ W per linear foot of cable.
        A. 100   C. 54
        B. 75   D. 25

_____ **20.** By definition, a place of assembly is a place designed for the assembly of ___ or more persons.
        A. 75   C. 200
        B. 100   D. 250

Name _____ Date _____

Time – 45 minutes

_____ 1. The minimum size THWN Cu ungrounded conductors required for a 200 A, 120/240 V, 1ϕ commercial service is #___.
   A. 1   C. 2/0
   B. 1/0   D. 3/0

_____ 2. Three resistors are connected in series across a 120 V supply. The voltage reading across R_1 and R_2 is zero. A voltage reading across R_3 is detected. The circuit fault is ___.
   A. R_3 is shorted   C. impedance blocked on R_1 and R_2
   B. R_3 is opened   D. R_3 is grounded

_____ 3. A metal octagon box contains two #12 and one #12 EGC. A lighting fixture is to be attached to the octagon box. The fixture has two #16 fixture wires and one #16 EGC. The minimum size box required is ___.
   A. 4″ × 1¼″   C. 4″ × 2⅛″
   B. 4″ × 1½″   D. neither A, B, nor C

_____ 4. Three resistors are connected in series across a 120 V supply. The voltage across R_1 is 0 V. The voltage across R_2 and R_3 is 60 V each. The circuit fault ___.
   A. R_1 is opened   C. R_3 is grounded
   B. R_1 is shorted   D. neither A, B, nor C

_____ 5. A dwelling unit has a 120/240 V, 300 A, 1ϕ service with THW Al conductors. The GES is a concrete-encased electrode. A #___ Cu GEC is required.
   A. 2   C. 1/0
   B. 6   D. 4

_____ 6. The power factor of a 5 kW, 1ϕ load drawing 30 A connected to a 208 V supply is ___%.
   A. 92   C. 80
   B. 84.5   D. 82.5

_____ 7. The minimum size metal device box required for four #12 ungrounded conductors, one grounded conductor, one GEC, and four #16 fixture wires is ___.
   A. 3″ × 2″ × 2¾″   C. 3″ × 2″ × 2¼″
   B. 3″ × 2″ × 2½″   D. 3″ × 2″ × 2″

_____ 8. A straight-through pull-box has a 2″ conduit with four #4/0 THW Cu conductors. The minimum length of the pull box is ___″.
   A. 24   C. 36
   B. 30   D. 16

_____ **9.** The minimum size box required for two #14 ungrounded conductors, two #14 grounded conductors, two #14 GECs, and two #16 fixture wires is ___ cu in.

    A. 13.5   C. 9

    B. 15.5   D. neither A, B, nor C

_____ **10.** The maximum unbalanced load in an apartment house is 250 A. The minimum computed load for the neutral is ___ A.

    A. 250   C. 235

    B. 104   D. neither A, B, nor C

_____ **11.** The minimum size conductor for an arc projector shall not be smaller than #___ AWG.

    A. 14   C. 10

    B. 12   D. 8

_____ **12.** A #8 AWG Cu conductor in a vertical raceway shall be supported every ___'.

    A. 100   C. 80

    B. 50   D. 25

_____ **13.** Vegetation shall not be used for the support of ___.

    A. boxes   C. overhead conductors

    B. lighting fixtures   D. raceways

_____ **14.** The ampacity of Type NM cable shall be based on ___.

    A. the size of NMS cable   C. 230.43

    B. a 40°C temperature rating   D. none of the above

_____ **15.** The thickness of ZFF fixture wire insulation is ___ mils.

    A. 30   C. 45

    B. 15   D. 14

_____ **16.** Conductors for hoistway door interlock wiring shall be Type ___ or equivalent.

    A. TW   C. SF

    B. THHN   D. XHHW

_____ **17.** Resistive heating elements shall be subdivided and shall not exceed ___ A.

    A. 48   C. 55

    B. 50   D. 60

_____ **18.** Live parts of a generator operating at more than ___ V to ground shall not be exposed to accidental contact.

    A. 50   C. 300

    B. 150   D. 480

_____ **19.** The nominal voltage for an alkali type battery shall be computed at ___ V per cell.

    A. 1.5   C. 2.5

    B. 2   D. 1.2

_____ **20.** The definition for _high voltage_ is listed in Article ___.

    A. 110   C. 490

    B. 100   D. 700

Name _____ Date _____

Time – 45 minutes

_____ 1. The minimum size box required for six #12 conductors, two internal cable clamps, and one SP switch is ___ cu in.
   - A. 12
   - B. 18
   - C. 15
   - D. 21

_____ 2. The area of allowable fill for a 1¼″ EMT conduit 23″ long is ___ sq in.
   - A. 1.38
   - B. 1.5
   - C. .6
   - D. .89

_____ 3. The minimum size IMC conduit for six #12 THW, six #12 TW, and three #10 THWN conductors is ___″.
   - A. ¾
   - B. 1
   - C. 1¼
   - D. 1½

_____ 4. The calculated amperage for a 10 kW, 240 V, 1φ strip heater is ___ A.
   - A. 41.7
   - B. 52
   - C. 55.6
   - D. 75

_____ 5. The minimum size OCPD required for the strip heater in Problem 4 is ___ A.
   - A. 50
   - B. 60
   - C. 70
   - D. 55

_____ 6. A 120/240 V, 1φ service with a computed load of 550 A and a 600 A OCPD requires ___ kcmil THWN Cu conductors paralleled.
   - A. 350
   - B. 250
   - C. 300
   - D. neither A, B, nor C

_____ 7. The GEC is a water pipe for the service in Problem 6. The minimum size Cu GEC required is #___.
   - A. 1/0
   - B. 2/0
   - C. 2
   - D. 3/0

_____ 8. In an apartment building with 60 units, each unit requires a 100 A, 1φ, 30-circuit MLO panel. The building service is a low-voltage wye distribution. The minimum size THW Cu ungrounded feeder conductors required for the unit panels are #___.
   - A. 4
   - B. 3
   - C. 1
   - D. neither A, B, nor C

_____ 9. Plans show a 200′ run of 1¼″ conduit with four #6 THW Cu conductors. Specifications require a pullbox every 100′ with splices in a J-box. A ___ J-box is required.
   - A. 4¹¹⁄₁₆″ × 2⅛″
   - B. 4″ × 4″ square
   - C. 6″ × 6″ square
   - D. neither A, B, nor C

_____ **10.** A piece of equipment on a branch circuit draws 16 A. The supply voltage is 208 V, 1φ. The length of the run is 165′. The minimum size Cu conductors required is #___. (Use approximate K.)

    A. 12   C. 8

    B. 10   D. 6

_____ **11.** The residual voltage of a capacitor shall be reduced to ___ V nominal or less within one minute after the capacitor is disconnected.

    A. 50   C. 120

    B. 80   D. 75

_____ **12.** Conductors for circuits operating at less than 50 V shall not be smaller than #___ AWG.

    A. 16   C. 14

    B. 18   D. 12

_____ **13.** A disconnecting means of adequate capacity for at least ___% of the input required for the momentary rating of X-ray equipment shall be provided in the supply circuit.

    A. 50   C. 80

    B. 125   D. 250

_____ **14.** The largest conductor permitted to be installed in a cellular concrete floor raceway is #___ AWG.

    A. 2/0   C. 3

    B. 1/0   D. 1

_____ **15.** A(n) ___ is a device without rotating parts that is sized for a given 3φ load and permits operation from a 1φ supply.

    A. rotary-phase converter   C. static-phase converter

    B. MG set   D. autotransformer

_____ **16.** An equipment enclosure containing a gasoline liquid is a ___ location.

    A. Class I, Div. 1   C. Class II, Div. 1

    B. Class I, Div. 2   D. Class III, Div. 1

_____ **17.** CATV stands for ___.

    A. cable antenna television   C. company antenna television

    B. community antenna television D. cable area television

_____ **18.** Optical fiber cables transmit ___ for communications.

    A. high voltage pulses   C. ion pulses

    B. low voltage pulses   D. light

_____ **19.** The high leg phase on a 3φ, 4-wire, delta-connected system shall be connected to the ___ phase.

    A. A   C. C

    B. B   D. N

_____ **20.** For X-ray installations, the long-time rating shall be based on an operating interval of ___ minutes or longer.

    A. 2   C. 4

    B. 3   D. 5

Name _____ Date _____

Time – 45 minutes

_____ 1. An installation has a 200 A switch, 150 A fuse, and #1/0 THWN Cu conductors. A #___ Cu EGC is required.
   A. 8
   B. 6
   C. 1/0
   D. 4

_____ 2. A branch circuit is protected by a 60 A fuse. The #6 THWN conductors are required to be increased to #4 due to voltage drop. The minimum size Cu EGC required is #___.
   A. 10
   B. 8
   C. 6
   D. neither A, B, nor C

_____ 3. A general lighting circuit is wired with #10 THWN Cu rated at 75°C. The maximum size OCPD permitted is ___ A.
   A. 35
   B. 25
   C. 30
   D. 40

_____ 4. A #10/2 Type NM cable has a bare EGC. The ampacity of the bare #10 conductor is ___ A.
   A. 50
   B. 25
   C. 30
   D. neither A, B, nor C

_____ 5. A 240 V, 1ϕ motor with a 29.4 A LRC has a maximum rating of ___ HP.
   A. ½
   B. ¾
   C. 1
   D. 1½

_____ 6. The AC resistance of 1000′ of #4/0 Cu in PVC is ___ Ω.
   A. .0608
   B. .062
   C. .015
   D. .0576

_____ 7. A 1ϕ transformer with a 120 V primary and a 12 V secondary has a rated output of .5 kW and is 95% efficient. The primary power is ___ VA.
   A. 526
   B. 500
   C. 475
   D. neither A, B, nor C

_____ 8. A 3-wire, 1ϕ branch circuit supplied from a 120/208 V subpanel, feeds two 15 A HID lighting circuits. The neutral shall be considered ___.
   A. carrying 0 A
   B. carrying 30 A
   C. a current-carrying conductor
   D. for derating

_____ 9. The ampacity of a 25 HP, 230 V synchronous motor at unity power factor is ___ A.
   A. 68
   B. 75
   C. 58
   D. 53

_____ 10. A total of ___ 15 A, 2-wire, 120 V lighting branch circuits are required to supply a show window 30′ long.
     A. three   C. five
     B. four   D. six

_____ 11. A minimum of ___ VA shall be required for each lot in a mobile home park.
     A. 16,000   C. 25,000
     B. 20,000   D. 30,000

_____ 12. The volume of a wiring enclosure (box) shall be based on the total ___.
     A. box size   C. volume of assembled sections
     B. box cubic inch size   D. number of conductors

_____ 13. Type MI cable shall be supported at intervals not exceeding ___′.
     A. 4   C. 6
     B. 4½   D. 5

_____ 14. A ___ is a DC device consisting of one or more 2-pole, 2-wire, nonpolarized, nongrounding-type receptacles intended to be used on DC circuits only.
     A. bull switch   C. 2-pole, 2-wire block
     B. DC spider   D. plugging box

_____ 15. ___ construction is a system in which the concealed parts of the processes of manufacture cannot be inspected without disassembly or damage.
     A. Closed   C. Open
     B. Concealed   D. Non-accessible

_____ 16. The OCPDs for #18 AWG stranded wire used in low-voltage circuit wiring for a park trailer shall not exceed ___ A.
     A. 15   C. 10
     B. 6   D. 8

_____ 17. Coaxial cable shall be separated at least ___″ from conductors of any electric light or power circuits.
     A. 6   C. 4
     B. 8   D. 10

_____ 18. The percent of fill for a raceway with one conductor is ___%.
     A. 53   C. 31
     B. 80   D. 40

_____ 19. The area within ___′ horizontally from aircraft power plants or aircraft fuel tanks shall be classified as a Class I, Division 2 location.
     A. 5   C. 8
     B. 10   D. 20

_____ 20. ___ is the portion of a property where flammable liquids are received by tank vessel, pipe line, or tank vehicle.
     A. A Class II, Division 1 plant   C. A fuel depot
     B. A bulk storage plant   D. A Class III storage depot

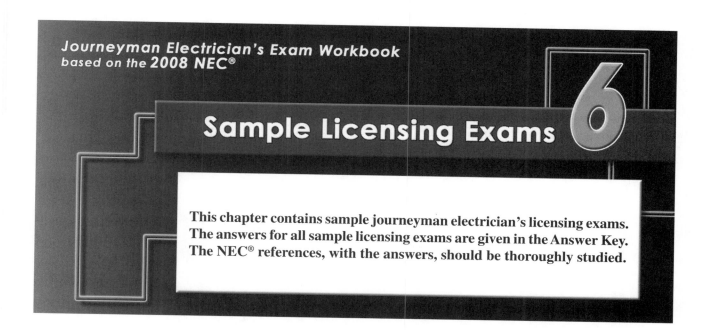

Sample Licensing Exams 6

This chapter contains sample journeyman electrician's licensing exams. The answers for all sample licensing exams are given in the Answer Key. The NEC® references, with the answers, should be thoroughly studied.

SAMPLE LICENSING EXAMINATIONS

The sample licensing examinations in this chapter are typical of the questions and problems found on examinations developed by the authority having jurisdiction or a private testing agency. Working these questions and problems will aid in preparing for the examination. Note that the questions and problems of the sample licensing exams in this chapter are sample questions only. These sample licensing exams are designed as open book tests.

Each sample licensing exam consists of 80 questions. Each exam contains questions based on trade knowledge, NEC® calculations, and questions from the NEC® Code book. Each sample licensing exam has a three hour time limit. This allows two minutes, fifteen seconds per question (3 hr = 180 min ÷ 80 questions = 2 min, 15 sec).

Examination Preparation

When preparing for an exam, it is important to learn as much as possible about the exam. It will help to obtain information from the certifying agency about the exam or talk with individuals who have successfully passed the exam. Also, verify that the exam is the correct exam for the certification expected.

Exam preparation should be paced. Spend time researching topics covered on the exam and develop a study schedule to focus on specific topics one at a time over an extended period of time. Review exam study materials over several days prior to the exam. Any review of the material the night before the exam should be limited. If unfamiliar with the exam location, drive to the site a few days before the exam date. Schedule a normal amount of sleep the night before the exam and allow ample time for traveling to the exam site.

While taking the exam, avoid being intimidated and remain calm. The necessary preparation for the exam has been completed, and now, that preparation will ensure the expected results. It is important to pace your work according to the time allotted. On the first pass through the questions, answer only the questions that can be answered with absolute certainty. If a question is skipped, be sure to skip that number on the answer sheet.

Read each question carefully and identify all possible answers. Know what is being asked before attempting to answer a question. Take time to verify that the proper answer blank has been filled in completely. If unsure of an answer, lightly mark the question number on the answer sheet. When finished with the other questions, return to the unanswered question and, if still unsure after checking the question again, eliminate the obvious incorrect answers. Make an educated guess using the remaining answers. Never leave an unanswered question.

When finished with the examination, review the entire exam and/or answer sheet for any missing information or answers, misplaced answers, or stray marks. The number of answers completed on the exam and/or answer sheet must match the number of questions.

Name _____ Date _____

Time – 180 minutes

_____ 1. The general lighting load for an assembly hall is calculated at ___ VA per square foot.
   A. 1   C. 3
   B. 2   D. 3½

_____ 2. The grounded conductor is ___ in color.
   A. green   C. orange
   B. gray   D. black

_____ 3. A ___ is not considered a wet location.
   A. glue house   C. garage
   B. cold storage warehouse   D. storage cellar

_____ 4. The minimum height for a fluorescent light in a tunnel operating at more than 277 V-to-ground is ___'.
   A. 22   C. 20
   B. 24   D. 18

_____ 5. Receptacles rated at 15 and 20 A, 125 V and installed ___ a kitchen countertop in a dwelling shall have GFCI protection.
   A. within 3' of the sink in   C. A and B
   B. within 6' of the sink in   D. neither A, B, nor C

_____ 6. The outlet for a washing machine in a dwelling unit shall be installed within ___' of the intended location.
   A. 0   C. 7
   B. 6   D. 8

_____ 7. Hallways in a dwelling unit ___' or more in length are required to have a receptacle outlet.
   A. 5   C. 10
   B. 8   D. neither A, B, nor C

_____ 8. A 125 V receptacle is required within ___' of an A/C unit installed on a flat roof of a duplex dwelling.
   A. 6   C. 10
   B. 75   D. neither A, B, nor C

_____ 9. In general, festoon lighting conductors shall not be smaller than #___.
   A. 12   C. 8
   B. 10   D. 16

_____ **10.** A(n) ___ is an aid in reducing arcing in movable contacts.

    A. spring   C. spark covers

    B. inductor   D. neither A, B, nor C

_____ **11.** ___ is/are used to obtain a separately derived system.

    A. Signaling   C. Solar power

    B. Motors   D. Transformers

_____ **12.** A metal raceway may require ___′ of clearance from a lightning rod conductor.

    A. 3   C. 6

    B. 10   D. 8

_____ **13.** The thickness of insulation for #12 RHH is ___ mils.

    A. 45   C. 20

    B. 30   D. neither A, B, nor C

_____ **14.** Ceiling fans that do not exceed ___ lb are permitted to be supported by an approved outlet box.

    A. 50   C. 40

    B. 30   D. 70

_____ **15.** A ⅜″ flexible fixture whip with outside fittings, containing three #12 THWN conductors (black, white, and bare), ___.

    A. is permitted   C. shall not be larger than ⅜″

    B. is not permitted   D. neither A, B, nor C

_____ **16.** The high leg shall be connected to Phase ___.

    A. A   C. C

    B. B   D. any phase, provided conductor is orange

_____ **17.** A total number of ___, 3-pole CBs may be installed in a panelboard.

    A. 42   C. 20

    B. 30   D. 14

_____ **18.** Drywall shall be repaired if there are open spaces at the edge of the box, greater than ___″.

    A. ¹⁄₁₆   C. ¼

    B. ⅛   D. neither A, B, nor C

_____ **19.** A gang of three switches in a box for 277 V lighting containing each of the three phase conductors requires ___.

    A. the grounded conductor to be labeled   C. colors to be brown, orange, and yellow

    B. each phase to be a different color   D. a barrier installed between switches

_____ **20.** The minimum size EGC for a swimming pool is #___.

    A. 8 solid Cu   C. 12 Cu

    B. 8 stranded Al   D. 10 Cu

_____ **21.** Switching devices on the property shall be located at least ___′ from the inside walls of a pool.

    A. 10   C. 15

    B. 20   D. 5

_____ **22.** Bathroom receptacles in a dwelling unit shall ___.

    A. be supplied by one 20 A circuit   C. have no other outlets

    B. be GFCI protected   D. A, B, and C

_____ **23.** A 50 A, 2-pole CB has a 60°C rating. The plans require all wiring to be THWN Cu. A #___ conductor is required.

    A. 8   C. 4

    B. 6   D. neither A, B, nor C

_____ **24.** A voltmeter is connected in ___ in a circuit.

    A. series   C. parallel

    B. series-parallel   D. wye

_____ **25.** Receptacles for rooftop A/C units shall be located within ___ of the unit.

    A. 25′   C. 50′

    B. insight   D. 75′

_____ **26.** ENT is not permitted to be used in ___.

    A. poured concrete   C. wet locations

    B. damp locations   D. direct earth burial

_____ **27.** For branch-circuit wiring located within a fire-rated drop ceiling, EMT shall be permitted to be attached to ceiling support wires by ___.

    A. approved clips   C. fire-rated ties

    B. steel tie wire   D. neither A, B, nor C

_____ **28.** PVC conduit shall be ___ to remove rough edges.

    A. reamed inside and trimmed outside   C. reamed

    B. trimmed inside and outside   D. trimmed

_____ **29.** The grounded terminal for a receptacle may be identified by ___.

    A. a metal coating white in color   C. the word white

    B. the letter W   D. A, B, and C

_____ **30.** The heating effect of 5 A of AC compared to 5 A of DC is ___.

    A. the same   C. 1.73 as great

    B. 1.41 as great   D. .707 as great

_____ **31.** A room containing a switchboard has a temperature of 38°C. This is a reading of ___°F.

    A. 96.4   C. 100.4

    B. 102.6   D. neither A, B, nor C

_____ **32.** A 240 V, 1ϕ feeder supplies a 2 HP, 3 HP, and 5 HP motor. In general, ___ A is the maximum size CB permitted for the feeder conductors.
    A. 85   C. 100
    B. 90   D. 110

_____ **33.** A 1200 VA, 240 V, 1ϕ load with an 85% power factor draws ___ A.
    A. 6   C. 4.25
    B. 5   D. 8

_____ **34.** A 3 HP, 120 V, 1ϕ motor is ___% efficient.
    A. 100   C. 90
    B. 85   D. 55

_____ **35.** A 300 A, 120/240 V, 1ϕ service for a dwelling requires a #___ Cu GEC when connected to a concrete-encased system ground.
    A. 2   C. 4
    B. 1/0   D. 3

_____ **36.** The maximum size CB permitted for short-circuit protection if a 2 HP, 208 V, 1ϕ motor starts and carries the load, is ___ A.
    A. 30   C. 40
    B. 35   D. 25

_____ **37.** The OCPD used for a 2 HP, 208 V, 1ϕ motor is not adequate for the motor to start. A ___ A TDF is permitted.
    A. 30   C. 40
    B. 35   D. 25

_____ **38.** The OCPD selected for a 2 HP, 208 V, 1ϕ motor is not sufficient to allow the motor to start. A ___ A CB is permitted.
    A. 35   C. 70
    B. 60   D. 50

_____ **39.** A dwelling has a floor area of 2300 sq ft plus a 150 sq ft garage. A total of ___ 15 A circuits are required for general lighting.
    A. six   C. four
    B. five   D. three

_____ **40.** A dwelling unit has a 240 V, 1ϕ A/C heat pump that draws 35 A. The unit contains 7.5 kW of supplementary heat. These loads will add ___ VA to the service calculation.
    A. 8400   C. 15,900
    B. 10,335   D. 7500

_____ **41.** A single-phase converter that supplies a variable load draws 34 A. The conductor ampacity is ___ A.
    A. 39.1   C. 37.4
    B. 85   D. 42.5

_____ **42.** A ___ conductor is a conductor intentionally connected to earth.
    A. phase   C. grounding
    B. grounded   D. grounding equipment

_____ **43.** A three-phase 30 HP, 460 V motor has a full-load current rating of ___ A.

    A. 32   C. 40

    B. 80   D. 88

_____ **44.** The minimum headroom of working space for a motor control center is ___′.

    A. 6   C. 7

    B. 6½   D. 8

_____ **45.** ___ can be connected to a small appliance circuit.

    A. A garbage disposal   C. Kitchen lighting

    B. A range hood   D. A dining room clock outlet

_____ **46.** Service-entrance conductors shall have clearance of ___′ from the bottom of a window.

    A. 3   C. 6

    B. 5   D. 4½

_____ **47.** The minimum size permitted of SJO or SJ cord supplying a water conditioner that is cord-and-plug-connected to a 20 A circuit is #___ AWG.

    A. 16   C. 14

    B. 18   D. 12

_____ **48.** ___ is the total resistance in a AC circuit.

    A. Reluctance   C. Impedance

    B. Mhos   D. Inductance

_____ **49.** ___ is not a standard ampere rating for fuses.

    A. Thirty-five   C. Forty

    B. Fifty   D. Fifty-five

_____ **50.** The ampacity of #8 AWG FEPB conductors in free air, rated less than 1000 V, is ___ A.

    A. 80   C. 70

    B. 60   D. 50

_____ **51.** The volume allowance required for a #12 AWG conductor in a box is ___ cu in.

    A. 1.5   C. 2.00

    B. 1.75   D. 2.25

_____ **52.** A disconnecting means shall be provided on the supply side of all fuses over ___ V to ground.

    A. 150   C. 50

    B. 120   D. 125

_____ **53.** The number of bends permitted in one run of RMC conduit is ___.

    A. 4/45   C. 6/45

    B. 4/90   D. 8/45

_____ **54.** The ampere rating of the disconnecting means for a hermetically sealed motor-compressor shall be based on ___% of the nameplate rated-load current.

    A. 110   C. 125

    B. 115   D. 250

_____ **55.** The length of a flexible cord supplying a swimming pool motor shall not exceed ___'.

    A. 3   C. 6

    B. 5   D. 4½

_____ **56.** One horsepower equals ___ W.

    A. 647   C. 746

    B. 476   D. 674

_____ **57.** Multiconductor non-power-limited fire alarm cable must be protected within ___ of the floor.

    A. 18″   C. 7′

    B. 6′   D. 24″

_____ **58.** The unit of measurement for power is the ___.

    A. volt   C. amp

    B. watt   D. ohm

_____ **59.** A grounding electrode conductor shall be connected to an effectively grounded metal water pipe within ___′ of the entrance point of a building.

    A. 5   C. 10

    B. 20   D. 12

_____ **60.** Underground cable wiring is not permitted within ___′ horizontally of the inside wall of a swimming pool.

    A. 10   C. 8

    B. 20   D. 5

_____ **61.** Where live parts of motors or controllers operating at over ___ V nominal to ground are exposed, a rubber insulating mat shall be provided.

    A. 50   C. 110

    B. 100   D. 150

_____ **62.** A 3 HP, 1ϕ, 208 V motor is rated at ___ FLA.

    A. 19.6   C. 17

    B. 18.7   D. 34

_____ **63.** The NEMA configuration for a 250 V, 20 A, 1ϕ receptacle is ___.

    A.   B.   C.   D.

_____ **64.** Rod and pipe electrodes shall not be less than ___′ in length.

    A. 10   C. 8

    B. 12   D. 6

_____ **65.** Direct-buried conductors emerging from grade level shall be protected at least ___' above the finished grade.

    A. 3   C. 3½

    B. 6   D. 8

_____ **66.** The sheath for Type MN cable shall extend not less than ___″ inside a non-metallic box.

    A. ⅜   C. ¼

    B. ½   D. ⅝

_____ **67.** In indoor wet locations where the walls are frequently washed down, raceways and boxes shall be mounted so that there is ___″ of air space between the boxes and the wall.

    A. ⅜   C. ¼

    B. 3⁄16   D. ⅛

_____ **68.** A luminaire (fixture) weighing more than ___ lb shall not be supported by the screw shell of the lampholder.

    A. 6   C. 8

    B. 3   D. 5

_____ **69.** The branch circuit supplying a fixed storage-type water heater that has a capacity of 120 gal. or less shall have a rating not less than ___% of the nameplate of the unit.

    A. 110   C. 125

    B. 115   D. 112

_____ **70.** A non-Type IC recessed luminaire (fixture) shall be spaced ___″ from combustible material.

    A. ½   C. 1

    B. ¾   D. ⅞

_____ **71.** The allowable ampacity for #14 AWG fixture wire is ___ A.

    A. 20   C. 17

    B. 15   D. 12

_____ **72.** LFMC shall be fastened within ___″ of a box.

    A. 8   C. 10

    B. 12   D. 6

_____ **73.** The ampacity for electric motors shall be based on ___.

    A. horsepower   C. NEC® tables

    B. volt-amps   D. service factor

_____ **74.** Conduit seals in Class I, Division 1, locations shall be installed within ___″ of pressurize enclosures.

    A. 12   C. 24

    B. 18   D. 10

_____ **75.** Each elevator car shall be supplied with ___ branch circuit(s) for lights, auxiliary lighting, and ventilation.

    A. one   C. three

    B. two   D. four

_____ **76.** In general, a mobile home power supply cord shall be rated at no more than ___ A.

    A. 60   C. 45

    B. 35   D. 50

_____ **77.** An outdoor dispensing device is classified as a Class ___, Division ___, location.

    A. I;1   C. II;1

    B. I;2   D. III;1

_____ **78.** In Class I, Division 1 and 2 locations, the sealing compound shall not be less than the trade size of the seal fitting and in no case less than ___".

    A. ⅝   C. ¾

    B. ½   D. ⅜

_____ **79.** On a separately derived system, the equipment grounding conductor for a swimming pool cannot be smaller than #___ AWG.

    A. 10   C. 8

    B. 6   D. 12

_____ **80.** Junction boxes shall be so installed that the wiring is ___.

    A. enclosed   C. rendered accessible

    B. covered   D. guarded

Sample Licensing Exam 6-2

Name _____ Date _____

Time – 180 minutes

_____ **1.** The rating of any one cord-and-plug connected appliance must not exceed ___% of the branch circuit rating.
    A. 50   C. 80
    B. 75   D. 150

_____ **2.** Flexible metal conduit used as a fixture whip to bond a fixture enclosure to a junction box shall not exceed ___'.
    A. 4   C. 6
    B. 8   D. 10

_____ **3.** Rigid metal conduit 1″ in diameter shall be supported every ___'.
    A. 10   C. 14
    B. 12   D. 20

_____ **4.** Liquidtight flexible metal conduit shall be used in ___″ minimum and ___″ maximum sizes.
    A. ½;4   C. ⅜;6
    B. ½;3   D. ½;6

_____ **5.** The minimum length of free conductor left at each outlet or junction box shall be ___″.
    A. 4   C. 8
    B. 6   D. 10

_____ **6.** The continuous current-carrying capacity of a 1″ square Cu bus bar mounted in an enclosure is ___ A.
    A. 500   C. 1000
    B. 750   D. 1500

_____ **7.** The maximum weight of a luminaire (light fixture) that may be mounted on the screw shell of a lampholder is ___ lb.
    A. 2   C. 10
    B. 6   D. 3

_____ **8.** Tubing having cut threads and used as arms or stems on light fixtures shall not be less than ___″ in wall thickness.
    A. .020   C. .040
    B. .025   D. .015

_____ **9.** Instruments, pilot lights, and potential transformers shall be protected by a ___ A OCPD or less.
    A. 15   C. 30
    B. 20   D. 50

_____ **10.** Overhead Cu conductors for systems of 600 V or less, and not over 50′ in length, shall be a minimum of #___.

        A. 14   C. 10

        B. 12   D. 8

_____ **11.** Branch-circuit conductors shall have an ampacity not less than the ___ load to be served.

        A. minimum   C. peak

        B. maximum   D. average

_____ **12.** The maximum number of overcurrent devices, other than mains, in a panelboard shall be based on ___.

        A. 24   C. panelboard design

        B. 36   D. 48

_____ **13.** The liquid in a battery is called ___.

        A. askarel   C. electrolyte

        B. hydrogen   D. base solution

_____ **14.** A megger is used for ___.

        A. reading high voltages   C. determining high resistance

        B. reading coulombs   D. determining high amperes

_____ **15.** FCC cable can be installed under carpet squares no larger than ___′ square.

        A. 1   C. 1½

        B. 2½   D. 3

_____ **16.** The maximum rating for a Edison-based plug fuse is ___.

        A. 20   C. 40

        B. 30   D. 35

_____ **17.** When the number of receptacles for an office building is unknown, an additional load of ___ VA per sq ft is required.

        A. 1   C. ½

        B. 2   D. 3

_____ **18.** A terminal for a grounded conductor on a polarized plug, when not visible, shall be ___.

        A. brass   C. marked with the word white

        B. marked green   D. neither A, B, nor C

_____ **19.** A reduction of ___ shall be used for a box containing one hickey and two clamps.

        A. one   C. three

        B. two   D. zero

_____ **20.** Raceways on the outside of a building shall be ___.

        A. weatherproof and covered   C. weatherproof and arranged to drain

        B. watertight and arranged to   D. rainproof and guarded
            drain

_____ **21.** The leads should be ___ when an ammeter is disconnected from a current transformer.

    A. taped off   C. grounded

    B. shorted   D. neither A, B, nor C

_____ **22.** Type SFF-1 wire should be limited to use where the voltage does not exceed ___ V.

    A. 500   C. 200

    B. 300   D. 600

_____ **23.** A header attaches to a floor duct at a ___ angle.

    A. 45°   C. right

    B. no angle specified   D. neither A, B, nor C

_____ **24.** Where conduit is threaded in the field, the cutting die should provide ___" taper per foot.

    A. ¼   C. ¾

    B. ½   D. no taper permitted

_____ **25.** Ranges and clothes dryers used in mobile homes shall be installed ___.

    A. per one-family dwellings   C. ungrounded

    B. with a neutral conductor   D. with a grounded and EGC

_____ **26.** ___ is not required on a motor nameplate.

    A. HP   C. Watts

    B. Manufacturer's identification   D. Voltage

_____ **27.** Underground conductors emerging from underground shall be in enclosures or raceways and shall be so enclosed to a point at least ___' above finished grade.

    A. 8   C. 10

    B. 6   D. 15

_____ **28.** In general, busways shall be supported at intervals not exceeding ___'.

    A. 3   C. 6

    B. 5   D. 10

_____ **29.** In general, voltage limitation between conductors in surface metal raceway is ___ V.

    A. 300   C. 1000

    B. 600   D. neither A, B, nor C

_____ **30.** The minimum size fixture wire is #___.

    A. 16   C. 14

    B. 18   D. 22

_____ **31.** A 240 V, 1φ branch circuit has a load of 15 A. Using #10 Al conductors, ___' is the maximum distance permitted for the run.

    A. 117.5   C. 255

    B. 193   D. 167

_____ **32.** A 5 HP, 200 V, 1φ motor has an FLC of ___ A.

    A. 56   C. 30.8

    B. 32.2   D. 28

_____ **33.** A branch circuit with a load of 41 A in an ambient temperature of 53°C requires #___ THWN Cu conductors.

    A. 8   C. 4
    B. 6   D. 3

_____ **34.** Two balanced 120/240 V, 1ϕ, 3-wire branch circuits are installed in ½″ conduit. The circuit conductors are #12 THW Cu. The ampacity of the ungrounded conductors is ___ A.

    A. 25   C. 17
    B. 15   D. 20

_____ **35.** The branch circuit computed load for the neutral of a 15 kW household range is ___ VA.

    A. 6440   C. 15,000
    B. 10,500   D. 9200

_____ **36.** A 240 V, 1ϕ transformer has a secondary current of 13 A. The rating of the transformer is ___ kVA. (Efficiency is 100%.)

    A. 1   C. 3
    B. 2   D. 4

_____ **37.** The resistance of 150′ of #8 stranded Al wire is ___ Ω.

    A. 192   C. 0.189
    B. 0.192   D. neither A, B, nor C

_____ **38.** A total of ___ #6 THHN Cu conductors are permitted to be installed in a 1¼″ EMT conduit 22″ long.

    A. 11   C. 17
    B. 12   D. 9

_____ **39.** Three loads are connected in series across a 120 V source. Each load has a resistance of 12 Ω with a current of 3.33 A. The total resistance of the circuit is ___ Ω.

    A. 3   C. 6.5
    B. 12   D. 36

_____ **40.** Three resistances 6 Ω, 9 Ω, and 12 Ω are connected in parallel across a 130 V source. The total resistance is ___ Ω.

    A. 2.78   C. 3
    B. 27   D. neither A, B, nor C

_____ **41.** The demand load for the service calculation for a dwelling unit that has a 5 kW central heat strip and a 5 HP, 240 V, 1ϕ, AC compressor is ___ VA. (optional method)

    A. 5000   C. 6720
    B. 3250   D. 11,000

_____ **42.** The maximum spacing between receptacles in a recreational vehicle is ___.

    A. 6′   C. 12′
    D. as per the furniture layout   D. no distance required

_____ **43.** ___ are not permitted to be used to mount electrical equipment in masonry.

    A. Rawl plugs   C. Plastic anchors
    B. Wooden plugs   D. Steel pins

_____ **44.** Switching devices shall be located at least ___' horizontally from the inside edge of a swimming pool.

A. 5   C. 10

B. 12   D. 6

_____ **45.** A ½" × 4" Cu busbar has ampacity of ___ A.

A. 200   C. 1400

B. 2000   D. 250

_____ **46.** Circuit breakers used to switch 277 V fluorescent lighting shall be marked ___.

A. with the GFCI rating   C. SWD

B. with a specified NEMA No.   D. for inductive loads only

_____ **47.** Conduit bodies in damp or wet locations shall be equipped so as to prevent ___ from entering the conduit body.

A. moisture   C. gases

B. vapors   D. fumes

_____ **48.** Nonmetallic auxiliary gutters shall be supported at intervals not to exceed ___' at each end or joint unless approved for other support intervals.

A. 4   C. 2

B. 3   D. 3½

_____ **49.** A(n) ___ switch shall be permitted to be used as both controller and disconnecting means on a circuit whose rating does not exceed 600 V or 100 A.

A. air-break   C. time delay

B. oil   D. auto-transformer type

_____ **50.** For circuits supplying loads consisting of motor-operated utilization equipment that is fastened in place and that has a motor larger than ___ HP in combination with other loads, the total computed load shall be based on 125% of the largest motor plus the sum of the other loads.

A. ⅛   C. ¼

B. ⅓   D. ½

_____ **51.** ___ means constructed so that exposure to weather such as rain will not interfere with successful operation.

A. Raintight   C. Rainproof

B. Weatherproof   D. Watertight

_____ **52.** The branch circuit ampacity for a 15 kW 110/220 V household electric range is ___ A.

A. 68   C. 62.5

B. 40   D. 50

_____ **53.** A 120:12 V, 1φ transformer that has a 500 VA secondary and is 95% efficient has ___ VA on the primary.

A. 500   C. 526

B. 495   D. 490

54. Overhead service drop conductors shall be___.
    A. insulated   C. fluorinated ethylene propylene
    B. noninsulated   D. A and B

55. Wiring located within the cavity of a fire-rated ceiling ___.
    A. can be attached to the ceiling   C. is not permitted
        support wires
    B. is permitted to support wiring   D. must have ⅟₁₆″ support wires
        if tested as a fire-rated assembly

56. A metal rack that supports and is in contact with electrical equipment ___.
    A. shall be grounded   C. does not require a grounding connection
    B. shall be grounded with an   D. A and B
        equipment grounding conductor

57. If a motor is connected by means of an attachment plug to a branch circuit that has no overload protection, the rating of the plug shall not exceed ___.
    A. 15 A/125 V   C. 20 A/125 V
    B. 20 A/250 V   D. 25 A/120 V

58. Type USE cable may have ___.
    A. a bare conductor   C. two insulated and one paper-
                        covered conductor
    B. an aluminum concentric   D. A and B
        conductor applied

59. The demand load for six 6 kW household electric dryers is ___ kW.
    A. 24   C. 27
    B. 28.5   D. 36

60. Single-conductor cable used for a carnival ride shall be permitted in sizes larger than #___.
    A. 2   C. 4
    B. 3   D. 6

61. The suffix 2 in RHW-2 conductors indicates ___.
    A. AWG size   C. mil size
    B. that it is permitted for   D. switchboard wiring only
        continuous use at 90°C

62. A luminaire (fixture) installed between 5′ and 10′ horizontally from the edge of a swimming pool shall have GFCI protection unless installed ___ above the maximum water level.
    A. 5′   C. 7′-6″
    B. 6′-7″   D. 7′

63. The maximum number of disconnecting means permitted for a service is ___.
    A. three   C. six
    B. one   D. two

_____ **64.** ENT threaded through metal framing using punched or factory holes shall be ___.
        A. protected by a bushing   C. sealed
        B. protected by a grommet   D. A and B

_____ **65.** An overhead 240 V span of an open conductor shall have a minimum diagonal clearance of ___' from a chimney.
        A. 6   C. 8
        B. 10   D. 3

_____ **66.** The main bonding jumper shall be made of ___, a corrosion-resistant metal.
        A. nickel   C. carbon
        B. copper   D. aluminum

_____ **67.** Locations protected from the weather, such as marquees and canopies, are considered ___ locations.
        A. dry   B. moist
        B. damp   D. wet

_____ **68.** A building under construction is considered a ___ location.
        A. dry   C. moist
        B. damp   D. wet

_____ **69.** An area used to wash vehicles is considered a ___ location.
        A. dry   C. moist
        B. damp   D. wet

_____ **70.** "In sight from" means visible at no less than ___'.
        A. 100   C. 50
        B. 75   D. 25

_____ **71.** Four hundred watts is ___ kVA.
        A. 400   C. .4
        B. 800   D. 40

_____ **72.** At the end of a raceway a ___ is not permitted to be used for splicing.
        A. box   C. cabinet
        B. bushing   D. panelboard

_____ **73.** Voltage drop in a wire is ___.
        A. wire resistance times voltage   C. skin effect
        B. a percentage of the applied   D. power times the voltage
           voltage

_____ **74.** The demand load for twenty-eight 8 kW household electric ranges is ___ kW.
        A. 53.76   C. 43
        B. 22.4   D. 56.45

_____ **75.** The approximate K factor for copper is ___.
        A. 12.9   C. 13.4
        B. 22.3   D. 44.2

_____ **76.** A circuit breaker shall be marked with the ___ in a manner that is durable and visible after installation.
    A. voltage rating   C. ampere rating
    B. interrupting rating   D. manufacturer name

_____ **77.** A cord-and-plug-connected ___ is not required to be grounded.
    A. dishwasher   C. electric toaster
    B. hedge clippers   D. aquarium pump

_____ **78.** RHH #12 AWG without outer covering has the same approximate area as ___.
    A. THW   C. XFF
    B. THHW   D. all of the above

_____ **79.** The rating of any one piece of cord-and-plug-connected utilization equipment shall not exceed ___% of the branch-circuit rating.
    A. 50   C. 35
    B. 80   D. 75

_____ **80.** The ___ conductor shall be connected to the screw shell.
    A. grounded   C. grounding
    B. ungrounded   D. equipment grounding

Name _____ Date _____

Time – 180 minutes

_____ 1. The allowable ampacity of #10 XF Cu wire is ___ A.
   A. 28   C. 25
   B. 30   D. 35

_____ 2. SJ cord is not permitted to be used for ___.
   A. extra-hard usage   C. damp locations
   B. hard usage   D. pendants

_____ 3. The maximum length of a flexible cord used to supply a room A/C with a nominal 120 V rating is ___'.
   A. 6   C. 10
   B. 4   D. 5

_____ 4. Optical fiber cables transmit ___ for control, signaling, and communications.
   A. electric impulses   C. electricity
   B. light   D. joules

_____ 5. The minimum headroom of the working space about service equipment, switchboards, or motor control centers shall be ___'.
   A. 8   C. 10
   B. 8½   D. 6½

_____ 6. The maximum size bored hole in a 2 × 4 stud for a raceway is ___".
   A. ¾   C. 1
   B. ⅞   D. 1¼

_____ 7. Except where computations result in a major fraction of an ampere ___ or larger, such fractions are allowed to be dropped.
   A. 0.5   C. 0.7
   B. 0.6   D. 0.8

_____ 8. Dry-type transformers installed indoors and rated 112½ kVA or less shall have a separation of at least ___" from combustible material.
   A. 6   C. 12
   B. 24   D. 10

_____ 9. Fittings of the ___ type are permitted for outdoor use.
   A. set-screw steel   C. set-screw die cast
   B. compression   D. all-steel bushing

_____ **10.** RNC is not permitted to be used for ___.
   A. direct burial   C. support fixtures
   B. in cinder fill   D. in ceilings

_____ **11.** The maximum trade size permitted for rigid metal conduit is ___″.
   A. 4   C. 5
   B. 6   D. 8

_____ **12.** The ___ is used to measure very high resistances.
   A. Wheatstone Bridge   C. VM
   B. ohmmeter   D. megger

_____ **13.** A voltmeter is calibrated to read the ___ value of AC.
   A. effective   C. peak
   B. true   D. maximum

_____ **14.** The maximum size OCPD permitted for #12 THHN Al with a load of 14 A is ___ A.
   A. 15   C. 25
   B. 20   D. 30

_____ **15.** Electrons flow ___.
   A. from positive to negative   C. counterclockwise
   B. from negative to positive   D. from neutrons to protons

_____ **16.** Two to six service disconnects shall be ___.
   A. approved for damp locations   C. grouped
   B. installed indoors   D. 3ϕ disconnects

_____ **17.** Temporary wiring for general illumination lampholders shall be ___.
   A. at least 10′ above finished floor   C. grounded
   B. weatherproof   D. guarded

_____ **18.** An underground feeder is installed in PVC. The circuit load is 84 A with a 100 A OCPD. The copper conductors are increased one size due to line loss. The minimum size EGC is #___.
   A. 8   C. 3
   B 6   D. 4

_____ **19.** A(n) ___ is not a grounding electrode system.
   A. ground ring   C. underground metal gas pipe
   B. metal water pipe   D. metal frame of a building

_____ **20.** UF cable shall not be permitted to be installed ___.
   A. as direct burial   C. in a cable tray
   B. as interior wiring   D. as service entrance cable

_____ **21.** Fixtures shall be so constructed or installed that adjacent combustible material is not subjected to temperatures in excess of ___°C.
   A. 75   C. 185
   B. 90   D. 140

_____ **22.** The maximum length of a bonding jumper outside of a raceway or enclosure is ___'.
    A. 3   C. 25
    B. 6   D. neither A, B, nor C

_____ **23.** Conductors, splices, and taps shall not fill a metal wireway to more than ___% of its area at that point.
    A. 25   C. 125
    B. 80   D. 75

_____ **24.** Weatherheads shall be listed ___.
    A. for wet location   C. rainproof
    B. weatherproof   D. watertight

_____ **25.** The ampacity of phase conductors from the generator terminals to the first overcurrent device shall not be less than ___% of the nameplate amperage rating of the generator.
    A. 75   C. 125
    B. 115   D. 140

_____ **26.** The minimum size building wire permitted to be used for a ten-story building is #___.
    A. 14   C. 16
    B. 12   D. 18

_____ **27.** The internal diameter of a 1″ rigid PVC conduit, Schedule 80 is ___″.
    A. 0.936   C. 1.255
    B. 1.049   D. 1.105

_____ **28.** ___ shall not be used in a damp or wet location.
    A. AC cable   C. EMT
    B. Open wire   D. Rigid conduit

_____ **29.** A(n) ___ is considered as two overcurrent devices.
    A. Edison-base fuse   C. lightning arrester
    B. 2-pole CB   D. shunt inductor

_____ **30.** Ground-fault protection that opens the service disconnecting means ___ protect service conductors or the service disconnecting means on the supply side.
    A. will   C. adequately
    B. will not   D. totally

THWN solid, uncoated Cu branch-circuit conductors sized for a 3% VD and serving a 2 HP, 240 V, 1ϕ motor are used with Problems 31 through 37.

_____ **31.** The FLC of the 2 HP motor is ___ A.
    A. 12   C. 13.2
    B. 13.8   D. 24

_____ **32.** The minimum size wire permitted for the motor is #___.
    A. 12   C. 8
    B. 10   D. 14

_____ **33.** The maximum ampacity permitted for overload protection is ___ A (based on FLC).

    A. 12   C. 15

    B. 13.8   D. 11.5

_____ **34.** The maximum NTDF permitted for the motor is ___ A.

    A. 30   C. 35

    B. 40   D. 50

_____ **35.** The maximum length of the branch-circuit conductors is ___'.

    A. 95.6   C. 57.3

    B. 98.6   D. 67

_____ **36.** The total resistance of the branch-circuit conductors is ___ Ω.

    A. .2348   C. .4412

    B. .75   D. .2935

_____ **37.** The output of the motor is ___ VA.

    A. 2880   C. 3600

    B. 1492   D. 3168

_____ **38.** The demand load for 28, 11 kW household ranges is ___ kW.

    A. 92.4   C. 43

    B. 73.9   D. 48.6

_____ **39.** The branch-circuit load for a built-in 3 kW deep fryer is ___ VA.

    A. 3000   C. 2400

    B. 1950   D. 3750

_____ **40.** A 4 Ω resistor is connected in series to a parallel branch that contains two 8 Ω resistors connected in parallel. The total resistance is ___ Ω.

    A. 12   C. 8

    B. 20   D. 4.8

_____ **41.** Before approaching a person who has received an electrical shock ___.

    A. be certain the electricity is   C. get a first aid kit
       OFF

    B. get the foreman   D. keep the person calm

_____ **42.** Unless a conductor material is selected, the NEC® calculations shall be based on ___ conductors.

    A. Cu-Al   C. Aluminum

    B. Copper/Clad and Cu   D. Cu

_____ **43.** A neon tester detects ___.

    A. if voltage is present   C. DC polarity

    B. if a circuit is AC or DC   D. all of the above

_____ **44.** Insulated equipment grounding conductors shall have an outer finish that is ___.

    A. white   C. red with a yellow stripe

    B. natural gray   D. green with a yellow stripe

_____ **45.** A solenoid is a(n) ___.
    A. electrically operated device   C. relay
    B. magneto   D. thermocouple

_____ **46.** Operating a 120 V light bulb with a voltage of 124 V results in ___.
    A. shorter bulb life   C. a blown fuse
    B. a tripped CB   D. dimmer light

_____ **47.** Soldering flux is used to ___.
    A. prevent corrosion   C. melt solder
    B. clean surfaces   D. cool a connection

_____ **48.** Hysteresis is ___.
    A. a lagging value resulting from   C. impedance
        a change in magnetism
    B. unwanted induced currents in   D. capacitance
        the core of a transformer

_____ **49.** The machine screw with the smallest diameter is ___.
    A. $^{10}/_{32} \times \frac{1}{2}''$ C. $^{8}/_{32} \times \frac{1}{2}''$
    B. $^{6}/_{32} \times \frac{1}{2}''$ D. $^{10}/_{24} \times \frac{1}{2}''$

_____ **50.** A chain wrench can be used ___.
    A. for different sizes of pipe   C. with one hand
    B. in tight places   D. either A, B, or C

_____ **51.** The best device used to recharge a battery is a(n) ___.
    A. AC generator   C. rectifier
    B. DC generator   D. capacitor

_____ **52.** A covered conductor is ___.
    A. encased in a material not   C. enclosed in a nylon jacket
        recognized as insulation
    B. enclosed in thermoplastic   D. an insulated conductor

_____ **53.** A continuous load is a load in which the maximum current is expected for ___ hr or more.
    A. 1   C. 6
    B. 8   D. 3

_____ **54.** Automatic is actuated by an impersonal influence such as ___.
    A. current   C. temperature
    B. pressure   D. all of the above

_____ **55.** ___ means constructed in such a way so that dust will not enter the enclosure.
    A. Dusttight   C. NEMA 3R rating
    B. Dustproof   D. Sealed

_____ **56.** A 15 kW household electric range has a branch-circuit rating of ___ A.
    A. 38   C. 50
    B. 40   D. 35

_____ **57.** A test light indicates ___.

      A. voltage   C. kVA

      B. amperes   D. continuity

_____ **58.** ___ conductors are service conductors installed between the weather head and the service equipment.

      A. Lateral   C. Service entrance

      B. Drop   D. Service tap

_____ **59.** Receptacles installed on a 15 A and 20 A branch circuits shall be ___.

      A. ungrounded   C. color coded

      B. grounded   D. specification grade

_____ **60.** The least important requirement to producing a good solder connection between two stranded conductors is ___.

      A. applying sufficient heat   C. twisting conductors together

      B. tinning each strand before   D. cleaning each strand
         soldering

_____ **61.** The demand load for a circuit that has a 5 kW heat strip and a 5 HP, 240 V compressor is ___ W.

      A. 3250   C. 6720

      B. 5000   D. 6250

_____ **62.** In a(n) ___ circuit, the continuity of the grounded conductor shall not depend on the removal of such devices that would interrupt the continuity of the circuit.

      A. branch   C. multiwire

      B. appliance   D. general purpose branch

_____ **63.** ___ is not permitted to be used for strain prevention on the joints or terminals of a cord-connected appliance.

      A. Knotting the cord   C. Winding the cord with
                                      tape

      B. A fittings approved for the   D. Nylon support string
         purpose

_____ **64.** A universal motor may not operate on ___.

      A. AC   C. AC or DC

      B. DC   D. variable frequency

_____ **65.** Twenty-eight 6 kW household electric ranges would have a demand load of ___ kW.

      A. 40.3   C. 36.96

      B. 43   D. 29.5

_____ **66.** A 350′ run supplying a 7 1/2 HP, 1ϕ, 240 V motor fed from a 3ϕ, 240 V panel requires #___ AWG Cu wire.

      A. 3   C. 4

      B. 6   D. 8

_____ **67.** A 4″ × ½″ copper busbar has an ampacity of ___ A.

    A. 2000   C. 1400

    B. 1500   D. 2500

_____ **68.** The minimum cubic inch capacity of a 4″ × 4″ × 1½″ square box is ___.

    A. 30.3   C. 18

    B. 21.5   D. 21

_____ **69.** ___ when working on a low-voltage circuit.

    A. Use insulated tools   C. Always assume the circuit is hot

    B. Do not work alone   D. Disconnect the load

_____ **70.** In a mobile home ___′ is the maximum spacing between receptacles.

    A. 6   C. 12

    B. 8   D. 10

_____ **71.** On a #4 drill, the number 4 indicates ___.

    A. strength   C. length

    B. diameter   D. hardness

_____ **72.** ___ is a protection technique permitted for equipment in Class I, Division 2, locations.

    A. Oil cutout   C. Oil immersion

    B. Oil-filled cutout   D. Interrupter switch

_____ **73.** Splices are permitted in all of the following except ___.

    A. panelboards   C. conduit bodies not marked with cubic inches

    B. J boxes   D. floor boxes

_____ **74.** ___ is not acceptable as an equipment grounding conductor.

    A. The armor of Type AC cable   C. A 30 A protected conductor in flexible metal conduit

    B. Intermediate metal conduit   D. Cablebus framework

_____ **75.** The overload protection for #12 AWG Cu wire is ___ A.

    A. 20   C. 30

    B. 25   D. 35

_____ **76.** The maximum motor running overcurrent protection for a 7½ HP, 1ϕ, 208 V motor is ___ A.

    A. 50.6   C. 57.2

    B. 44   D. 55

_____ **77.** Type S fuse adapters are designed so they ___.

    A. cannot be removed   C. can be removed easily

    B. can be installed in parallel   D. can be removed with a special tool

_____ **78.** A 5 kW cooktop and a 4 kW oven have a demand load of ___ W.

    A. 9000   C. 5850

    B. 8000   D. 11,000

_____ **79.** The ampacity for each of three #12 AWG XHHW Cu conductors in a wet location is ___ A.

    A. 20   C. 30

    B. 25   D. 35

_____ **80.** Attachment plugs shall be constructed so that there are no exposed current-carrying parts except ___.

    A. prongs   C. pins

    B. blades   D. A, B, and C

Name _____ Date _____

Time – 180 minutes

_____ 1. A kW is ___.
   A. 1000 W
   B. 100 VA
   C. 10 kVA
   D. for rating motors

_____ 2. If you add ten duplex receptacles for general lighting in a dwelling this would increase the service load calculation by ___ kW.
   A. 1.8
   B. 10
   C. 0
   D. 1.2

_____ 3. Type MV Cable shall have ___ conductors.
   A. copper
   B. aluminum
   C. copper-clad aluminum
   D. A, B, or C

_____ 4. A solenoid is a(n) ___.
   A. relay
   B. permanent magnet
   C. photo cell
   D. electromagnet

_____ 5. The standard size overcurrent protection for #6 TW Cu wire is ___ A.
   A. 60
   B. 55
   C. 70
   D. 75

_____ 6. Field assembled extension cord sets having #___ or larger conductors shall be considered to be protected by 20 A branch-circuit protection.
   A. 16
   B. 18
   C. both A and B
   D. neither A nor B

_____ 7. ___ is permitted to be installed in a cable tray.
   A. Power and control tray cable
   B. MI cable
   C. PVC conduit
   D. A, B, or C

_____ 8. The largest conductor permitted to be installed in a hollow space of a cellular metal floor is #___.
   A. 1/0
   B. 6
   C. 8
   D. 10

_____ 9. An AC transformer welder shall have an OCPD rated or set at not more than ___% of the rated primary current of the welder.
   A. 125
   B. 80
   C. 300
   D. 200

_____ 10. The maximum size Cu GEC required for a service is ___.
  A. 250 kcmil   C. 600 kcmil
  B. #3/0   D. 300 kcmil

_____ 11. Fixtures or lampholders shall have no live parts normally exposed to contact unless they are ___ type.
  A. rosette   C. cleat
  B. recess   D. neither A, B, nor C

_____ 12. A rating of ___ A is not a standard size fuse.
  A. 110   C. 75
  B. 125   D. 250

_____ 13. Multiple grounding electrodes shall be not less than ___′ apart.
  A. 6   C. 12
  B. 10   D. neither A, B, nor C

_____ 14. Conductors, #___ and larger, shall be stranded when installed in raceways.
  A. 8   C. 4
  B. 6   D. 10

_____ 15. ___ is permitted to be attached to a riser conduit used to support a service drop.
  A. Telephone service cable   C. either A or B
  B. Cable TV service   D. neither A or B

_____ 16. Temporary power for christmas lights is permitted for a period not to exceed ___ days.
  A. 90   C. 120
  B. 60   D. 30

_____ 17. A counter space in a kitchen ___″ or wider requires a receptacle.
  A. 12   C. 20
  B. 24   D. neither A, B, nor C

_____ 18. ___ small appliance circuit(s) is/are required for a kitchen.
  A. One   C. Three
  B. Two   D. Four

_____ 19. Romex can be used on multifamily dwellings and structures for Types ___ construction.
  A. II and III   C. II, III, and V
  B. I, II, and III   D. III, IV, and V

_____ 20. The NEC® is intended to be suitable for mandatory application by inspecting authorities over ___.
  A. electrical installations   C. both A and B
  B. railroad installations   D. neither A nor B

_____ 21. The alternating current GEC is sized by the ___.
  A. service main disconnect   C. service overcurrent size
  B. service drop conductors   D. neither A, B, nor C

_____ **22.** Torque, repulsion, and induction are terms used with ___.
       A. ballasts   C. motors
       B. transformers   D. generators

_____ **23.** A total of ___° of bends are permitted in a run of EMT.
       A. 360   C. 320
       B. 180   D. 240

_____ **24.** In general, conductor size for a single motor shall have an ampacity not less than ___% of the FLC rating.
       A. 110   C. 125
       B. 115   D. 0

_____ **25.** For stationary motors of ⅛ HP or less and 300 V or less, a ___ may serve as the disconnecting means.
       A. HP-rated switch   C. CB
       B. fuse   D. either A, B, or C

_____ **26.** A space of ___′ or more shall be provided between the top of any switchboard and any combustible ceiling.
       A. 3   C. 4
       B. 6   D. 2

_____ **27.** The smallest wall space requiring a receptacle is ___′.
       A. 2   C. 5
       B. 3   D. 6

_____ **28.** The total 100% area for a ½″ flexible metal conduit is ___ sq in.
       A. .630   C. .317
       B. .632   D. .622

_____ **29.** ___ size box is required for 30.3 cubic inches of conductor fill.
       A. 4 × 1¼″ sq   C. FD 2⅛″
       B. 4 × 2⅛″ sq   D. 3¾ × 2 × 3½″ masonry

_____ **30.** Shore-power receptacles shall be rated not less than ___ A.
       A. 20   C. 40
       B. 30   D. 50

_____ **31.** An apartment building has ten 12 kW ranges and eight 14 kW ranges. The demand load is ___ kVA.
       A. 36.3   C. 33
       B. 18   D. 34.65

_____ **32.** The demand load for sixteen 6 kW household ranges is ___ kW.
       A. 26.9   C. 96.0
       B. 48.5   D. 96.5

_____ **33.** The FLC of a 240 V, 5 HP DC motor is ___ A.
       A. 15   C. 10
       B. 20   D. 12.9

_____ **34.** A 1 HP, 230 V motor draws 4 A. The power consumed by internal losses is ___ VA.
    A. 920   C. 746
    B. 174   D. 1666

_____ **35.** The demand load for nine 10 kW household ranges is ___ kVA.
    A. 25   C. 24
    B. 31.5   D. 28.3

_____ **36.** A 3 Ω, 6 Ω, and 9 Ω resistor is connected in parallel. R_T is ___ Ω.
    A. 1.64   C. .61
    B. 18   D. neither A, B, nor C

_____ **37.** A 3 Ω, 6 Ω, and 9 Ω resistor is connected in series. R_T is ___ Ω.
    A. 1.64   C. .61
    B. 18   D. 2.64

_____ **38.** Six #10 THWN Cu current-carrying conductors are installed in a raceway. The ambient temperature is 105°F. The ampacity of the conductors is ___ A.
    A. 23   C. 28.7
    B. 35   D. 28

_____ **39.** A heat pump and A/C unit draws 28 A at 240 V, 1ϕ. The A/H contains a 240 V, 7.5 kW heat strip. A total of ___ VA is added to the service load calculation.
    A. 6720   C. 14,220
    B. 7500   D. 9243

_____ **40.** A 120 V, 1ϕ branch circuit with a 12 A load has a 116′ run. Number ___ Cu conductors are required.
    A. 12   C. 8
    B. 10   D. 14

_____ **41.** A nipple can be ___.
    A. threaded both ends   C. not threaded
    B. threaded one end   D. all of the above

_____ **42.** The best way to charge a battery is by using a(n) ___.
    A. DC motor   C. wheatstone bridge
    B. rectifier   D. AC to DC generator

_____ **43.** ___ may be used to mount a box to a hollow block wall.
    A. Toggle bolts   C. Lag bolts
    B. Wood plugs   D. Concrete anchors

_____ **44.** When mounting a panel, ___ shall not be used.
    A. toggle bolts   C. concrete anchors
    B. wood plugs   D. threaded rod

_____ **45.** A 5 kW cooktop and a 6 kW oven has a demand load of ___ kW.
    A. 9000   C. 8000
    B. 7150   D. 1100

_____ **46.** The primary current is ___ A.

    A. 2.5   C. 25

    B. .3   D. 30

120 V   12 V   300 W

_____ **47.** Service-entrance cable used for interior wiring shall comply with ___.

    A. Article 314   C. Part I and II of Article 334

    B. not permitted   D. Annex C

_____ **48.** The turns ratio of this transformer is ___.

    A. 10:1   C. 10:2

    B. 1:10   D. 1:12

120 V   12 V

_____ **49.** Electrical equipment secured to and in contact with a metal rack or structure provided for its support shall be considered ___.

    A. secured   C. bonded

    B. effectively grounded   D. effectively attached

_____ **50.** Conduits through which moisture may contact energized parts shall be ___ at either or both ends.

    A. open   C. sealed

    B. arranged to drain   D. threaded

_____ **51.** On a single-pole switch, the terminals are required to be ___.

    A. not identified   C. marked SWD

    B. identified   D. colored coded

_____ **52.** A Type AC cable run across the top of floor joists or within ___' of the floor in attics shall be protected by guard strips.

    A. 6   C. 10

    B. 7   D. not required

_____ **53.** Clearance for conductors not over 600 V from signs and radio and television antennas shall not be less than ___'.

    A. 3   C. 6

    B. 8   D. 3½

_____ **54.** The overload protection for #12 RHH AWG Cu is ___ A.

      A. 30   C. 25

      B. 20   D. 35

_____ **55.** In sight from is equipment not more than ___′ from other equipment.

      A. 100   C. 50

      B. 75   D. 25

_____ **56.** Circuit breakers shall be marked for ___ rating.

      A. interrupting   C. voltage

      B. current   D. A, B, and C

_____ **57.** An existing luminaire (fixture) between 5′ and 10′ from the edge of a pool shall not be less than ___′ above the maximum water level.

      A. 5   C. 10

      B. 6   D. 8

_____ **58.** Rigid nonmetallic conduit shall not be used ___.

      A. in hazardous locations   C. in theaters

      B. for support of a luminaire   D. A, B, and C

_____ **59.** ___ shall not be used for the connection between a grounding conductor and a grounding electrode.

      A. Pressure connectors   C. Listed lugs

      B. Exothermic welding   D. Solder

_____ **60.** The parts of a swimming pool requiring bonding shall be connected to a common bonding grid with a(n) ___ copper conductor not smaller that #8 AWG.

      A. covered   C. solid

      B. insulated   D. all of the above

_____ **61.** Where multiple rod, pipe, and plate electrodes are used, they shall not be less than ___′ apart.

      A. 6   C. 15

      B. 10   D. 12

_____ **62.** A rectifier converts ___.

      A. DC to AC   C. magnetism to energy

      B. AC to DC   D. wattage to apparent power

_____ **63.** In a raceway containing eight current-carrying conductors, the ampacity shall be derated by ___%.

      A. 80   C. 50

      B. 70   D. 45

_____ **64.** A 480 V transformer with a 240/120 V secondary has no 240 V load. The secondary has 6 kW from A–N and 6 kW from B–N. The neutral is ___.

      A. the same size as the ungrounded conductor   C. no relation to the ungrounded conductor

      B. 70% smaller than the ungrounded conductor   D. 50% smaller than the ungrounded conductor

65. Two small appliance circuits, one laundry circuit, one 12 kW range, one 4 kW dryer, one 1.2 kW dishwasher, and four 1920 VA lighting loads are fed from a 3-wire, 240/120 V, 1φ source. Choice ___ is the best correct balanced load condition.

A.		B.		C.		D.	
1500	1500	1500	1920	1200	1200	1500	1920
1500	1920	1500	1920	1200	1920	1500	1920
1920	1920	1500	1920	1200	1920	1500	1920
6000	6000	6000	6000	4000	4000	1500	1920
2000	2000	4000	4000	2500	2500	1920	1200
1920	1200	1920	1200	1920	1200	4000	4000

66. The kVA input is mostly near ___ kVA if the transformer load is 500 VA.
    A. 1500
    B. 500
    C. .5
    D. .05

67. Using the standard calculation Part I and III of Article 220, the A/C is calculated for the service at ___%.
    A. 80
    B. 125
    C. demand factor
    D. full load

68. The NEC® allows noncontinuous metal raceways between J boxes, cabinets, and enclosures if ___.
    A. EMT raceway is used for surge protection
    B. rigid metal conduit is used for temporary power
    C. flexible metal conduit is used for motors
    D. short section are used for cable protection

69. THW Cu wire run through a fluorescent luminaire (fixture) shall have a temperature rating not lower than ___°C.
    A. 90
    B. 60
    C. 75
    D. 175

70. ___ sets of #1 THW Cu are permitted to be run in parallel.
    A. One
    B. Two
    C. Three or more
    D. Zero

71. To prevent ___ when working in a room full of batteries, caution should be taken not to cause sparks.
    A. a fire
    B. an explosion
    C. contact pitting
    D. an electric shock

72. Improper makeup of splices and connections ___.
    A. violates NEMA standards
    B. violates ANSI standards
    C. causes heat
    D. increases circuit capacitance

73. Lampholders used in branch circuits having a rating in excess of ___ A shall be of the heavy-duty type.
    A. 12
    B. 15
    C. 16
    D. 20

_____ **74.** The demand load for a 14 kW household range is ___ kW.

    A. 8.8   C. 12

    B. 14   D. 9.8

_____ **75.** The demand for an 8 kW household electric range is calculated at 6.4 kW. The neutral load would be ___ kW.

    A. 4.48   C. 8

    B. 6.4   D. 5.6

_____ **76.** The neutral current is ___ A.

    A. 53.3   C. 0

    B. 45   D. 8.33

$120/240\ 1\phi$

A   N   B

6400 VA   5400 VA

_____ **77.** The demand load for two 4.5 kVA household electric dryers is ___ kVA.

    A. 10   C. 9

    B. 7   D. 6.3

_____ **78.** A string of outdoor lights that is suspended between two points is ___ lighting.

    A. outline   C. festoon

    B. carnival   D. car lot

_____ **79.** Nichrome® wire is used in toasters over copper because ___.

    A. it makes better toast   C. it has higher resistance

    B. of cost   D. it has lower resistance

_____ **80.** Two 1½ HP, 115 V, 1ϕ motors require #___ THW Cu conductors.

    A. 12   C. 8

    B. 10   D. 6

Definitions
2

REVIEW 2-1 _____ 19

Definitions (100)

1. **D**
2. **A**
3. **C**
4. **B**
5. **D**
6. **C**
7. **C**
8. **D**
9. **B**
10. **A**
11. **D**
12. **D**
13. **C**
14. **A**
15. **B**
16. **A**
17. **D**
18. **D**
19. **A**
20. **B**

REVIEW 2-2 _____ 21

Definitions (100)

1. **D**
2. **C**
3. **B**
4. **C**
5. **A**
6. **C**
7. **A**
8. **A**
9. **B**
10. **D**
11. **D**
12. **C**
13. **B**
14. **D**
15. **C**
16. **A**
17. **B**

18. **A**
19. **B**
20. **D**

Electrical Formulas
3

REVIEW 3-1 _____ 39

Electrical Formulas

1. **C** Electrical theory
2. **A** Electrical theory
3. **B** *210.19(A), FPN 4*
4. **D** Electrical theory
5. **C** Electrical theory
6. **C** $P_T = I^2 \times R$
$P_T = (25)^2 \times 21 = 13,125$
$P_T = \textbf{13,125 W}$

7. **D** $Output = HP \times 746$
$Output = 5 \times 746 = 3730$
$Output = \textbf{3730 VA}$

8. **D** $R = \dfrac{E_2}{P}$
$R = \dfrac{240 \times 240}{10,000}$
$R = \dfrac{57,600}{10,000} = 5.76$
$R = \textbf{5.76 } \Omega$

9. **D** *Ch 9, Table 8:*
    #1 Cu = .154 Ω/kFT
    #1 Cu = 83,690 CM
$K = \dfrac{R \times CM}{1000}$
$K = \dfrac{.154 \times 83,690}{1000}$
$K = \dfrac{12,888.26}{1000} = 12.88$
$K = \textbf{12.88 } \Omega$

10. **C** *Ch 9, Table 8:*
    250 kcmil = **250,000**

11. **D** $Cost = \dfrac{T \times W \times Cost / kWh}{1000}$
$Cost = \dfrac{8 \times 200 \times .09}{1000}$
$Cost = \dfrac{144}{1000} = 14.4$
$Cost = \textbf{\$0.14}$

12. **C** $R_T = R_1 + R_2 + R_3$
$R_T = 4 + 6 + 8 = 18$
$R_T = \textbf{18 } \Omega$

13. **A** $R_T = \dfrac{1}{\dfrac{1}{R_1} + \dfrac{1}{R_2} + \dfrac{1}{R_3}}$
$R_T = \dfrac{1}{\dfrac{1}{4} + \dfrac{1}{6} + \dfrac{1}{8}}$
$R_T = \dfrac{1}{.250 + .167 + .125}$
$R_T = \dfrac{1}{.542} = 1.845$
$R_T = \textbf{1.845 } \Omega$

14. **D** $HP = \dfrac{I \times E \times E_{ff}}{746}$
$HP = \dfrac{28 \times 240 \times .55}{746}$
$HP = \dfrac{3696}{746} = 4.9$
$HP = \textbf{5 HP}$

15. **A** $I_P = \dfrac{kVA \times 1000}{E_P}$
$I_P = \dfrac{1500}{120} = 12.5$
$I_P = 12.5 \text{ A}$
450.3(B), Ex.:
    12.5 A × 125% = 15.6 A
240.6: Next higher rating = 20 A
OCPD = **20 A**

16. **D** $VD = \dfrac{K \times I \times D}{CM}$
$VD = \dfrac{42.4 \times 40 \times 210}{16,510}$
$VD = \dfrac{356,160}{16,510} = 21.57$
$VD = \textbf{21.57 V}$

17. **A** $R_p = \dfrac{R_1 \times R_2}{R_1 + R_2}$

   $R_p = \dfrac{4 \times 3}{4 + 3}$

   $R_p = \dfrac{12}{7} = 1.7$

   $R_p = 1.7 \ \Omega$
   $R_T = 3 \ \Omega + 1.7 \ \Omega$
   $R_T = \mathbf{4.7 \ \Omega}$

18. **C** $R_p = \dfrac{1}{\dfrac{1}{R_1} + \dfrac{1}{R_2} + \dfrac{1}{R_3}}$

   $R_p = \dfrac{1}{\dfrac{1}{2} + \dfrac{1}{5} + \dfrac{1}{10}}$

   $R_p = \dfrac{1}{.5 + .2 + .1}$

   $R_p = \dfrac{1}{.8} = 1.25$

   $R_p = 1.25 \ \Omega$
   $R_T = 1.25 \ \Omega + 6 \ \Omega$
   $R_T = \mathbf{7.25 \ \Omega}$

19. **B** busbar ampacity = t × w × constant
   busbar ampacity = .5 × 4 × 700
   busbar ampacity = **1400 A**

20. **D** busbar ampacity = t × w × constant
   busbar ampacity = .25 × 4 × 1000
   busbar ampacity = **1000 A**

REVIEW 3-2 _____ 41
Electrical Formulas

1. **D** $I = \dfrac{P}{E}$

   $I = \dfrac{300}{130} = 2.3$

   $I = \mathbf{2.3 \ A}$

2. **C** $E = I \times R$
   $E = 1.5 \times 40 = 60$
   $E = 60 \ V$

   $I = \dfrac{E}{R}$

   $I = \dfrac{60}{50} = 1.2$

   $I = \mathbf{1.2 \ A}$

3. **A** $R_T = R_1 + R_2 + R_3$
   $R_T = 8 + 8 + 8 = 24$
   $R_T = \mathbf{24 \ \Omega}$

4. **A** $R_T = \dfrac{R_1}{N}$

   $R_T = \dfrac{8}{3} = 2.66$

   $R_T = \mathbf{2.66 \ \Omega}$

5. **B** $R_T = \dfrac{R_1 \times R_2}{R_1 + R_2}$

   $R_T = \dfrac{5 \times 10}{5 + 10}$

   $R_T = \dfrac{50}{15} = 3.33$

   $R_T = \mathbf{3.33 \ \Omega}$

6. **C** $E = I \times R$
   $E = 4 \times 10 = 40$
   $E = \mathbf{40 \ V}$

7. **C** Electrical theory

8. **C** °F = (1.8 × °C) + 32
   °F = 1.8 × 30 + 32
   °F = 54 + 32 = 86
   °F = **86°F**

9. **A** $°C = \dfrac{°F - 32}{1.8}$

   $°C = \dfrac{104 - 32}{1.8}$

   $°C = \dfrac{72}{1.8} = 40$

   °C = **40°C**

10. **D** Electrical theory
11. **B** 210.19(A): FPN 4:
       240 V × .03 = **7.2 V**

12. **B** $VD = \dfrac{\text{Line Loss}}{\text{Supply Voltage}} \times 100$

   $VD = \dfrac{8}{115} \times 100 = 6.96$

   VD = **6.96%**

13. **B** $E_{ff} = \dfrac{\text{Output}}{\text{Input}}$

   $E_{ff} = \dfrac{295}{300} = 98$

   E_{ff} = **98%**

14. **A** $I = \dfrac{P}{E}$

   $I = \dfrac{6500}{115} = 56.62$

   $P = E \times I$
   $P = 120 \times 56.52 = 6782.4$
   $P = 115 \times 56.52 = 6499.8$
   $P = 6782.4 - 6499.8 = 282.6$
   P = 283 W
   or
   $P = E \times I$
   $P = 5 \times 56.52 = 282.6$
   P = 283 W

15. **B** Electrical theory
16. **A** Electrical theory
17. **C** 60 m × 3.28084′ = **196′**
18. **A** 24″ × 2.54 cm = **69.96 cm**
19. **C** $R_2 = \dfrac{R}{N}$

   $R_2 = \dfrac{12}{6} = 2$

   $R_T = R_1 + R_2$
   $R_T = 12 + 2 = \mathbf{14\Omega}$

20. **A** $R_p = \dfrac{1}{\dfrac{1}{R_1} + \dfrac{1}{R_2} + \dfrac{1}{R_3}}$

   $R_p = \dfrac{1}{\dfrac{1}{5} + \dfrac{1}{7} + \dfrac{1}{9}}$

   $R_p = \dfrac{1}{.2 + .142 + .111}$

   $R_p = \dfrac{1}{.453} = 2.2$

   $R_p = 2.2 \ \Omega$
   $R_T = 2.2 \ \Omega + 8 \ \Omega$
   $R_T = \mathbf{10.2 \ \Omega}$

REVIEW 3-3 _____ 43
Electrical Formulas

1. **B** $R = \dfrac{P}{S}$

   $R = \dfrac{120}{12} = 10$

   R = **10:1**

2. **D** $I = \dfrac{P}{E}$

   $I = \dfrac{300}{12} = 25$

   $I = \mathbf{25 \ A}$

3. **C** $kVA = \dfrac{I_s \times E_s}{1000}$

   $kVA = \dfrac{25 \times 12}{1000}$

   $kVA = \dfrac{300}{1000} = .03$

   kVA = **.3 kVA**

4. **C** $I_p = \dfrac{kVA \times 1000}{E}$

   $I_P = \dfrac{.3 \times 1000}{120}$

   $I_P = \dfrac{300}{120} = 2.5$

   $I_P = \mathbf{2.5 \ A}$

5. **B** $R = \dfrac{E_2}{P}$

   $R = \dfrac{12 \times 12}{300}$

   $R = \dfrac{144}{300} = .48$

   $R = \mathbf{.48 \ \Omega}$

6. **C** Electrical theory
7. **A** Electrical theory
8. **C** Electrical theory
9. **C** Electrical theory
10. **C** The 120 V loads are in series across
        240 V.

11. **A** $R = \dfrac{E_2}{P}$

$R = \dfrac{120 \times 120}{25}$

$R = \dfrac{14,400}{25} = 576$

$R = \mathbf{576\ \Omega}$

12. **B** $R = \dfrac{E_2}{P}$

$R = \dfrac{130 \times 130}{100}$

$R = \dfrac{16,900}{100} = 169$

$R = \mathbf{169\ \Omega}$

13. **A** $R_T = R_1 + R_2$
$R_T = 576 + 169 = 745$
$R_T = \mathbf{745\ \Omega}$

14. **C** $I = \dfrac{E}{R}$

$I = \dfrac{240}{745} = .322$

$I = \mathbf{.322\ A}$

15. **D** $E = I \times R$
$E = .322 \times 576 = 185.5$
$E = \mathbf{185.5\ V}$

16. **A** $E = I \times R$
$E = .322 \times 169 = 54.4$
$E = \mathbf{54.4\ V}$

NEC® Examples 4

REVIEW 4-1 _____ 59
NEC® Examples

1. **B** *Table 310.16*
2. **B** *Trade knowledge*
3. **D** *430.6(A)(1)*
4. **A** *220.12*
5. **D** *Ch 9, Note 4*
6. **A** *Annex C, Table C1*
7. **A** *Annex C, Table C8*
8. **A** *Table 310.15(B)(2)*
9. **A** *Ch 9, Table 4*
10. **D** *Trade knowledge*
11. **D** *250.52(A)(3)*
12. **D** *Ch 9, Table 5*
13. **C** *Ch 9, Table 8*
14. **C** *430.22(A)*
15. **C** *Table 310.15(B)(6)*
16. **A** *220.12*
17. **D** *700.9(D)*
18. **A** *324.41*
19. **B** *392.3(B)(1)*
20. **D** *406.8(E)*

REVIEW 4-2 _____ 61
NEC® Examples

1. **C** *240.6(A)*
2. **D** *Ch 9, Table 8*
3. **A** *210.19(A)(3)*
4. **B** *Ch 9, Table 8*
5. **D** *Table 430.248:*
    5 HP, 208 V = 30.8 A
    FLC = **30.8 A**

6. **D** *430.52; Table 430.52:*
    30.8 A × 250% = 77 A
    240.6: Next higher standard size = 80 A
    ITCB = **80 A**

7. **A** *430.6(A)(1):* Nameplate rating = 28 A
    Overload Protection = **28 A**

8. **A** *Ch 9, Table 8:* #12 stranded
    Cu = 1.98 Ω/1000'

    $\dfrac{1.98}{1000} = .00198\ \Omega/ft$

    $\dfrac{.41}{.00198} = 207'$

    Length = **207'**

9. **D** *Table 430.248:*
    3 HP = 17 A
    1 HP = 8 A
    430.62(A): 17 A × 250% = 42.5 A

	L1	N	L2
3 HP, 240 V	45	0	45
1 HP, 240 V	16	0	16
Total	61	0	61

    (not permitted to go to next higher size)
    240.6: 60 A
    ITCB = **60 A**

10. **B** *430.24:* 17 A × 125% = 21 A

	L1	N	L2
3 HP, 240 V	21	0	21
1 HP, 240 V	16	0	16
Total	37	0	37

    Ampacity = **37 A**

11. **B** *Table 310.16:*
    #6 RHW Al = 50 A
    Table 310.16, Correction Factors:
    50 A × 75% = 37.5 A
    Ampacity = **37.5 A**

12. **D** *Table 310.15(B)(2) Ex 3, 240.4(D):*
    OCPD = **30 A**

13. **C** *Table 220.55, Note 4;*
    Table 220.55, Col. C:
    One range = 8 kW
    Load = **8 kW**

14. **A** *430.6(A)(1); Table 430.248:*
    3 HP, 240 V = 17 A
    Ampacity = **17 A**

15. **A** *Table 220.55, Notes 1 & 2:*

8 × 14 kW	=	112 kW
5 × 12 kW	=	60 kW
10 × 12 kW	=	120 kW
Total	=	292 kW

    292 kW ÷ 23 = 12.7 kW
    (exceeds 12 kW by 1)
    23 ranges = 38 kW
    38 kW × 105% = 39.9 kW
    Demand Load = **39.9 kW**

16. **D** *Table 310.16:*
    100 A × 58% = 58 A
    Ampacity = **58 A**

17. **C** *450.4(A)*
18. **B** *525.5(B)*
19. **A** *500.5(B)(1) FPN 1, 2*
20. **D** *590.3(D)*

REVIEW 4-3 _____ 63
NEC® Examples

1. **B** *220.82(C)(2);*
    Annex D, Example D2(c):
    P = E × I
    P = 30 × 240 = 7200
    P = 7200 VA
    7200 VA + 7500 VA = 14,700 VA
    14,700 VA × 100% = 14,700 VA
    Load = **14,700 VA**

2. **A** *220.82(C)(1) and (4)*
    P = E × I
    P = 45 × 240 = 10,800
    P = 10,800 VA
    15,000 VA × 65% = 9750 VA
    220.60: Smaller load = 9750 V (omit smaller load)
    Load = **10,800 VA**

3. **A** *220.12:*
    General Lighting:

1900 sq ft × 3	=	5700 VA
Small Appl and Laundry	=	4500 VA
Total	=	10,200 VA

    Table 220.42:

3000 × 100%	=	3000 VA
7200 VA × 35%	=	2520 VA
Total	=	5520 VA

    Neutral Load = **5520 VA**

4. **C** *Table 430.248:*
    5 HP = 28 A
    3 HP = 17 A
    Table 430.52:
    5 HP = 28 A × 250% = 70 A
    430.62(A): 70 A + 17 A = 87 A

	L1	N	L2
5 HP, 240 V	70	0	70
3 HP, 240 V	17	0	17
Total	87	0	87

    240.6: CB = **80 A**

5. **B** 430.24:
 28 A × 125% = 35 A
 35 A + 17 A = 52 A

	L1	N	L2
5 HP, 240 V	35	0	35
3 HP, 120 V	17	0	17
Total	52	0	52

 Ampacity = **52 A**

6. **C** Table 310.15(B)(6): 225 A requires 250 kcmil
 Conductors = **250 kcmil**

7. **B** 220.12: 2200 sq ft × 3 VA = 6600 VA

 $I = \dfrac{VA}{V}$

 $I = \dfrac{6600}{120} = 55$

 55 A ÷ 15 A = 3.6 (round to 4)
 Circuits = **4**

8. **A** Ch 9, Table 8:
 Ω/kFT = per 1000 ft
 1.21 Ω ÷ 1000' = .0021 Ω/ft
 .00121 Ω × 90 = .1089 Ω
 Resistance = **.1089 Ω**

9. **B** 220.82(C)(1) and (4): Annex D, Example D2(c):
 A/C = 5760 W (omit smaller load)
 Heat = 10,000 VA × 65% = 6500 VA or 6.5 kVA
 Added Load = **6500 VA**

10. **C** 220.54:
 Dryer load = 5000 VA

 $I = \dfrac{VA}{V}$

 $I = \dfrac{5000}{240} = 20.8$

 I = 20.8 A
 220.61(B): 20.8 A × 70% = 14.6 A
 Added Load = **14.6 A**

11. **D** Annex C, Table C2:
 Seven #10 in ½"
 Conductors = **7**

12. **A** Table 220.55, Col B:
 7000 VA × 80% = 5600 VA

 $I = \dfrac{VA}{V}$

 $I = \dfrac{5600}{240} = 23.3$

 I = 23 A

13. **B** Ch 9, Table 5A:
 #1 = .415"
 Diameter = **.415"**

14. **C** Ch 9, Table 1:
 3 conductors = 40% fill
 Ch 9, Table 4:
 3" EMT conduit = 3.54
 Fill = **3.54 sq in.**

15. **C** 220.82(B)(3):
 Use nameplate rating
 kW = **12 kW**

16. **B** Table 220.55, Col A; 220.61(B):
 8000 W × 70% = 5600 W
 or 5.6 kW
 kW = **5.6 kW**

17. **C** Table 550.31
18. **C** 725.21(A)
19. **D** 408.36(C)
20. **A** 90.6

Review Questions 5

1. **B** Table 314.16(A)
2. **A** Trade knowledge
3. **A** Electrical theory
4. **A** Electrical theory
5. **C** 210.62
6. **A** 310.4
7. **B** 210.52(H)
8. **C** 210.52(B)(2), Ex. 1
9. **B** 220.12
10. **A** 220.14(G)
11. **C** Electrical theory
12. **D** 300.4(G)
13. **D** 250.53
14. **A** 110.14(A)
15. **B** 314.27(B)
16. **A** 430.6(A)
17. **A** 310.15(B)(6)
18. **B** Electrical theory
19. **A** 680.23(A)(4)
20. **B** 518.1

1. **B** Electrical theory
2. **A** Electrical theory
3. **B** 225.26
4. **C** 600.5(A)
5. **B** Electrical theory
6. **D** 100
7. **C** Electrical theory
8. **D** Electrical theory
9. **D** Trade knowledge
10. **A** Electrical theory
11. **D** Trade knowledge
12. **C** Electrical theory
13. **A** Trade knowledge
14. **A** Electrical theory
15. **A** Electrical theory
16. **C** Electrical theory
17. **C** Trade knowledge
18. **C** Trade knowledge
19. **A** Trade knowledge
20. **B** Electrical theory

1. **C** Table 310.13
2. **D** 300.22(A)
3. **B** Electrical theory
4. **B** 250.136(A)
5. **D** 680.26(B)(5)(1)
6. **C** 480.2
7. **C** 90.2(B)(2)
8. **B** Table 551.73
9. **D** 336.104
10. **A** 210.19(A)(3)
11. **D** 225.6(A)(1)
12. **A** 225.7(C)
13. **D** 230.71(A)
14. **A** Table 310.16
15. **D** 250.52(A)
16. **C** Table 310.13
17. **B** 334.80; Table 310.16
18. **A** Table 310.16
19. **C** Electrical theory
20. **B** Electrical theory

1. **C** 300.5(G)
2. **B** 370.4(C)
3. **B** 445.13
4. **B** Electrical theory
5. **D** Electrical theory
6. **C** Electrical theory
7. **B** 408.3(E)
8. **A** 314.21
9. **B** 376.22(B)
10. **C** 430.2
11. **A** 240.51(A)
12. **A** Table 312.6(B)
13. **B** 90.5(C)
14. **C** Trade knowledge
15. **C** 210.8(B)(1)
16. **D** 210.52(C)(1)
17. **C** 210.52(A)(3)
18. **A** 220.43(B)
19. **C** Table 402.5
20. **B** 342.14; 344.14

1. **B** 230.24(B)(4)
2. **B** 230.24(B)(2)
3. **A** 450.21(A)
4. **C** 334.23(A)
5. **B** Electrical theory
6. **A** Electrical theory
7. **A** 358.20(B)
8. **D** 424.3(B)
9. **D** 210.52(B)(1)
10. **C** Table 300.5
11. **B** 230.82(4)
12. **A** 110.14(B)
13. **A** 250.20(B)
14. **A** 230.53
15. **C** Table 300.19(A)

16. **C** *210.12(B)*
17. **A** *300.6(D)*
18. **A** *210.52(C)(5)*
19. **A** *440.64*
20. **B** *250.70(1)*

REVIEW 5-6 _____ 81

1. **B** *700.12(A)*
2. **B** *225.6(A)(1)*
3. **C** *230.7, Ex. 1*
4. **A** *630.11(A)*
5. **B** *540.13*
6. **C** *110.34(C)*
7. **C** *240.30(A)(1)*
8. **C** *250.102(A)*
9. **D** *110.13(A)*
10. **A** *404.8(A)*
11. **D** *338.10(B)(1)*
12. **A** *Table 312.6(A)*
13. **A** *Table 310.15(B)(6)*
14. **C** *250.24(C)(1)*
15. **A** *100*
16. **B** *90.2(A)(B)(C)*
17. **B** *382.30*
18. **D** *230.51(A)*
19. **B** Trade knowledge
20. **C** Electrical theory

REVIEW 5-7 _____ 83

1. **D** Electrical theory
2. **B** Electrical theory
3. **C** Electrical theory
4. **A** Electrical theory
5. **B** Electrical theory
6. **A** *Table 300.5*
7. **C** *Table 250.122*
8. **D** Electrical theory
9. **C** Electrical theory
10. **A** *310.13*
11. **A** *410.10(D)*
12. **B** *314.28(A)(2)*
13. **C** *250.64(E)*
14. **A** *250.64(A)*
15. **B** *230.9(A), Ex.*
16. **C** *Table 250.66*
17. **D** *300.22(B)*
18. **A** *300.4(A)(1)*
19. **D** *110.15*
20. **B** Trade knowledge

REVIEW 5-8 _____ 85

1. **B** *100*
2. **C** Electrical theory
3. **A** Electrical theory
4. **D** Electrical theory
5. **A** Electrical theory
6. **C** Electrical theory
7. **A** Electrical theory
8. **C** Trade knowledge
9. **D** Electrical theory
10. **D** *410.56(E)*
11. **B** *424.35*
12. **C** *240.6(A)*
13. **D** Electrical theory
14. **C** 210.21(B)(1)
15. **C** *424.3(B)*
16. **B** *250.56*
17. **C** Electrical theory
18. **D** *Ch 9, Table 5*
19. **B** Electrical theory
20. **A** *Table 300.5*

REVIEW 5-9 _____ 87

1. **C** Electrical theory
2. **A** *422.16(B)(1)(2)*
3. **D** *460.8(A)*
4. **A** Electrical theory
5. **A** *540.13*
6. **C** *310.3*
7. **B** Electrical theory
8. **C** Electrical theory
9. **B** Electrical theory
10. **C** *410.75*
11. **B** *90.6*
12. **A** *410.68*
13. **D** Electrical theory
14. **B** Electrical theory
15. **A** Electrical theory
16. **B** *550.2*
17. **D** *90.1(B)*
18. **C** Electrical theory
19. **D** *Table 220.54*
20. **B** *240.22*

REVIEW 5-10 _____ 89

1. **B** *240.53(A)*
2. **B** Electrical theory
3. **C** *Table 220.12*
4. **A** Trade knowledge
5. **A** *344.42(B)*
6. **C** *500.5(C)*
7. **A** *250.140*
8. **B** *Table 314.16*
9. **D** Electrical theory
10. **A** *404.2(A)*
11. **A** Electrical theory
12. **A** *404.14(B)(2)*
13. **D** *Table 300.5*
14. **C** Electrical theory
15. **B** Trade knowledge
16. **C** *310.15(B)(3); Table 310.16*
17. **C** Electrical theory
18. **B** Electrical theory
19. **B** *310.4(E)*
20. **C** *422.13*

REVIEW 5-11 _____ 91

1. **A** *358.42*
2. **B** *332.40(B)*
3. **D** *Art 100*
4. **A** *Table 310.15(B)(2)(a)*
5. **C** *Table 314.16(A)*
6. **A** *250.22(3); 668.3(C)(3)*
7. **D** *680.23(A)(3)*
8. **A** *Table 348.22*
9. **A** *210.4(C)*
10. **C** Electrical theory
11. **C** *300.7(A)*
12. **B** Electrical theory
13. **C** *408.18(A)*
14. **D** *110.13(B)*
15. **C** *314.5*
16. **B** *220.14(H)(2)*
17. **D** *230.6(1)*
18. **A** *314.29*
19. **D** *220.12*
20. **D** *230.82(1-7)*

REVIEW 5-12 _____ 93

1. **D** *250.56, FPN*
2. **C** *Table 300.19(A)*
3. **A** *352.12(D)*
4. **D** *Ch 9, Table 1*
5. **D** *240.10*
6. **B** *410.16(C)(2)*
7. **B** *422.16(B)(2)(2)*
8. **B** *220.82(C)(4)*
9. **C** *Table 310.16; 240.4(B)*
10. **D** *680.26(B)*
11. **C** Electrical theory
12. **D** Electrical theory
13. **C** *220.14(I)*
14. **D** *Table 220.56*
15. **B** *400.8(1)*
16. **D** Electrical theory
17. **D** Trade knowledge
18. **C** Trade knowledge
19. **C** Trade knowledge
20. **A** Electrical theory

REVIEW 5-13 _____ 95

1. **D** *Table 250.66:*
   Over 350 kcmil Cu – 600 kcmil
   Cu = #1/0
   Cu GEC = **#1/0**

2. **A** *630.11(A):* Nameplate primary
   current based on duty cycle.
   90 A × 55% = 49.5 or 50 A
   Supply Conductors = **50 A**

3. **B** *314.16; Tables 314.16(A) & (B):*
   #14   2 × 2 = 4.00 cu in.
   #12   3 × 2.25 = 6.75 cu in.
   One EGC   = 2.25 cu in.
   One receptacle   = 4.50 cu in.
   Two cable clamps = 2.25 cu in.
                              19.75 cu in.
   Device Box = **19.75 cu in.**

4. **D** 314.16; Tables 314.16(A) & (B):

#12	$4 \times 2.25 =$	9 cu in.
EGC	$=$	2.25 cu in.
		11.25 cu in.

314.16(B)(1), Ex.: Less than five fixtures wires do not count.
Device Box = **11.25 cu in.**

5. **C** Table 310.16:
   #10 THWN Cu = 35 A
   Table 310.16, Correction Factors:
   32°C = .94
   35 A × .94 = 32.9 A
   Table 310.15(B)(2)(a):
   32.9 A × 80% = 26.3 A
   Conductors = **26.3 A**

6. **A** $I = \dfrac{P}{E}$

   $I = \dfrac{1500}{120} = 12.5$

   I = 12.5 A
   Table 430.248:
   One 2 HP, 230 V motor = 12 A
   Table 430.248:
   Three 1 HP, 120 V motors = 16 A
   430.24: 12 A × 125% = 15 A

L1	N	L2
12.5	0	12.5
15	0	15
16	0	16
	16	16
43.5	16	59.5

   Neutral = **16 A**

7. **B** 348.22: Two #12 XHHW conductors permitted. *In addition, one uninsulated EGC of same size shall be permitted.
   Conduit = **fitting outside**

8. **C** 630.11(A): 40 A × 78% = 31.2 A
   FLC = **31 A**

9. **D** 630.12(A): 40 A × 200% = 80 A
   OCPD = **80 A**

10. **D** 460.8(A): 18 A × 135% = 24.3 A
    Ampacity = **24.3 A**

11. **A** Table 400.4
12. **B** 440.4(C)
13. **D** 600.5(B)(2)
14. **D** 800.2
15. **C** 404.2(B)
16. **B** Article 555.2
17. **B** 410.53
18. **A** Table 326.24
19. **C** 424.44(A)
20. **B** 518.1

REVIEW 5-14 _____ 97

1. **D** Table 310.16:
   THWN Cu 200 A = #3/0
   Ungrounded Conductors = **#3/0**

2. **B** R_3 is open.
   Circuit Fault = **opened**

---

3. **A** 314.16(B)(1), Ex.;
   Table 314.16(A); Table 314.16(B):

#12	$2 \times 2.25 =$	4.5
#12 (EGC)	$1 \times 2.25 =$	2.25
#16 (Omit)		
		6.75

   Table 314.16(A):
   Octagon Box = **4″ × 1¼″**

4. **B** R_1 is shorted.
   Circuit Fault = **shorted**

5. **D** 250.66(B):
   GEC = **#4**

6. **C** $PF = \dfrac{P}{I \times E}$

   $PF = \dfrac{5000}{30 \times 208}$

   $PF = \dfrac{5000}{6240} = .80$

   PF = **80%**

7. **A** Table 314.16(A):
   4 #12 phase conductors
   1 #12 neutral
   314.16(B)(5): 1 #12 EGC
   314.16(B)(1), Ex.: Fixture wires require no deduction
   Table 314.16(A):
   6 #12 requires 3″ × 2″ × 2¾″
   Device Box = **3″ × 2″ × 2¾″**

8. **D** 314.28(A)(1): 8″ × 2″ = 16″
   Length = **16″**

9. **D** 314.16(A)(B); Table 314.16(A) & (B):

#14 Ungrounded conductor	$2 \times 2 =$	4
#14 Grounded conductor	$2 \times 2 =$	4
# 14 EGC	$=$	2
Total	$=$	10

   Box = **10 cu in.**

10. **C** 220.61(B)(2):

250 A – 200 A	$=$	50 A
50 A × 70%	$=$	35 A
200 A + 35 A	$=$	235 A

   Load = **235 A**

11. **D** 540.13
12. **A** Table 300.19(A)
13. **C** 225.26
14. **D** 334.80
15. **B** Table 402.3
16. **C** 620.11(A)
17. **A** 424.22(B)
18. **A** 445.14
19. **D** 480.2
20. **C** 490.2

REVIEW 5-15 _____ 99

1. **D** 314.16; Table 314.16(A):

Cable clamps	$=$	1 conductor
Six #12	$=$	6 conductors
SP switch	$=$	2 conductors
Total	$=$	9 conductors

   Table 314.16(A):
   Nine #12 = 21
   Box = **21 cu in.**

---

2. **D** Ch 9, Note 4; Ch 9, Table 4:
   1.496 × 60% = .89
   Fill = **.89 sq in.**

3. **B** Ch 9, Table 5:

#12 TW	$6 \times .0181$	= .1086
#12 THW	$6 \times .0181$	= .1086
#10 THWN	$3 \times .0211$	= .0633
Total		= .2805

   Ch 9, Table 1:
   Over 2 conductors = 40%
   Ch 9, Table 4: IMC = .384
   Conduit = **1″**

4. **A** I = W ÷ E
   I = 10,000 ÷ 240 = 41.7
   I = **41.7 A**

5. **B** I = W ÷ E
   I = 10,000 ÷ 240 = 41.7 A
   I = 41.7 A
   424.3(B): 41.7 A × 125% = 52 A
   240.6: 60 A
   OCPD = **60 A**

6. **C** Table 310.16:
   THWN 300 kcmil = 285 A
   285 A × 2 = 570 A
   240.6: Standard ratings = 500 A, 600 A
   240.4(B)(2):
   THWN 300 kcmil
   Conductors = **300 kcmil**

7. **A** Ch 9, Table 8:
   300,000 CM × 2 = 600,000 CM (600 kcmil)
   Table 250.66 : #1/0
   GEC = **#1/0**

8. **B** Table 310.15(B)(6):
   Low-voltage wye is a 120/208 V system. Table 310.15(B)(6) can only be used for 120/240 V systems.
   Feeder Conductors = **#3**

9. **A** Table 314.16(A):
   4¹¹⁄₁₆″ × 2⅛″ box
   J-box = **4¹¹⁄₁₆″ × 2⅛″**

10. **C** Ch 9, Table 8:
    1φ Cu = 25.8 Ω
    210.19(A), FPN 4:
    208 V × 3% = 6.24 V

    $CM = \dfrac{K \times I \times D}{VD}$

    $CM = \dfrac{25.8 \times 16 \times 65}{6.24}$

    $CM = \dfrac{68,112}{6.24} = 10,9153$

    Ch 9, Table 8:
    #8 Cu = 16,510 CM
    Conductors = **#8 Cu**

11. **A** 460.6(A)
12. **D** 720.4
13. **A** 660.5
14. **B** 372.10
15. **C** 455.2

16. **A** *Table 514.3(B)(1)*
17. **B** *Article 820*
18. **D** *770.6*
19. **B** *408.3(E)*
20. **D** *517.2*

REVIEW 5-16 _____ 101

1. **B** *Table 250.122:*
    EGC based on size of OCPD
    150 A fuses require #6 Cu
    EGC = #6 Cu

2. **B** *250.122(A):*
    EGCs shall be adjusted for VD:
    #8 Cu
    EGC = #8 Cu

3. **C** *240.4(D):*
    #10 limited to 30 A OCPD
    OCPD = 30 A

4. **C** *310.15(B)(3):*
    Conductor = 30 A

5. **A** *Table 430.251(A):* ½ HP
    Rating = ½ HP

6. **B** *Ch 9, Table 9:* .062 Ω
    Resistance = .062 Ω

7. **A** $Input = \dfrac{Output}{E_{ff}}$

    $Input = \dfrac{500}{.95} = 526$

    Power = 526 VA

8. **C** *310.15(B)(4)(b):*
    Neutral = **current-carrying**

9. **D** *Table 430.250:*
    25 HP motor = 53 A
    Ampacity = 53 A

10. **B** *220.14(G)(1):*
    30′ × 200 W = 6000 W

    $I = \dfrac{P}{E}$

    $I = \dfrac{6000}{120} = 50$

    $I = 50\ A$

    $\dfrac{50\ A}{15\ A} = 3.3$

    Circuits = 4

11. **A** *550.31(1)*
12. **C** *314.16(A)*
13. **C** *332.30*
14. **D** *530.2*
15. **A** *545.2*
16. **B** *552.10(E)(1)*
17. **C** *820.44(F)(1)*
18. **A** *Ch. 9, Table 1*
19. **A** *513.3(C)*
20. **B** *515.2*

SYMBOLS

'	feet	–	minus	¢	cents		concrete
"	inches	x	times	$	dollars	=	ground
#	number	÷	divided by	°F	degrees Fahrenheit	Ω	ohms
%	percent	=	equals	°C	degrees Celsius	φ	phase
+	plus	√	square root		steel		

FORMULAS . . .

EFFICIENCY

$$E_{ff} = \frac{Output}{Input}$$

$$Input = \frac{Output}{E_{ff}}$$

$$Output = \frac{Input}{E_{ff}}$$

$$E_{ff} = \frac{HP \times 746}{I \times E}$$

$$HP = \frac{I \times E \times E_{ff}}{746}$$

$$I = \frac{HP \times 746}{E \times E_{ff}}$$

POWER FACTOR
(Watts/Meter Reading)

$$PF = \frac{P}{E \times I}$$

$$PF = \frac{P_T}{P_A}$$

$$PF = \frac{R}{Z}$$

POWER
(SINGLE–PHASE)

$$P = E \times I$$

$$P = I^2 \times R$$

$$P = \frac{E^2}{R}$$

$$E = \sqrt{P \times R}$$

$$E = \frac{P}{I \times PF}$$

$$I = \frac{P}{E \times PF}$$

$$I = \sqrt{\frac{P}{R}}$$

$$R = \frac{E^2}{P}$$

$$R = \frac{P}{I^2}$$

OHMS LAW

$$E = I \times R$$

$$R = \frac{E}{I}$$

$$I = \frac{E}{R}$$

HORSEPOWER

746 watts = 1 HP

BUS BAR CAPACITY

thickness × width = square inches

square inches × 1000 = Cu ampere ampacity

square inches × 700 = AL ampere ampacity

ENERGY COST

$$cost = \frac{watts \times hours\,used \times cost\,per\,kWh}{1000}$$

SERIES CIRCUITS

$$E_T = E_1 + E_2 + E_3 + \ldots$$

$$I_T = I_1 = I_2 = I_3 = \ldots$$

$$R_T = R_1 + R_2 + R_3 + \ldots$$

PARALLEL CIRCUIT RESISTANCE

$$R_T = \frac{1}{\dfrac{1}{R_1} + \dfrac{1}{R_2} + \dfrac{1}{R_3}}$$

$$R_T = \frac{R_1 \times R_2}{R_1 + R_2}$$

$$R_T = \frac{R_1}{N}$$

PARALLEL CIRCUIT
VOLTAGE AND CURRENT

$$E_T = E_1 = E_2 = E_3 = \ldots$$

$$I_T = I_1 + I_2 + I_3 + \ldots$$

TEMPERATURE CONVERSION

$$°F = (1.8 \times °C) + 32$$

$$°C = \frac{°F - 32}{1.8}$$

VOLTAGE DROP

$$VD = \frac{K \times I \times D}{CM}$$

$$CM = \frac{K \times I \times D}{VD}$$

$$I = \frac{VD \times CM}{D \times K}$$

$$D = \frac{CM \times VD}{K \times I}$$

$$VD = \frac{line\,loss}{supply\,voltage} \times 100$$

TRANSFORMERS
SINGLE–PHASE

$$kVA = \frac{I_P \times E_P}{1000}$$

$$kVA = \frac{I_S \times E_S}{1000}$$

$$I_P = \frac{kVA \times 1000}{E_P}$$

$$I_S \frac{I_P \times E_P}{E_S}$$

TRANSFORMER POWER
(100% EFFICIENT)

$$E_P \times I_P = E_S \times I_S$$

TRANSFORMER TURNS

$$T_P = \frac{I_S \times T_S}{I_P}$$

$$T_S = \frac{E_s \times T_P}{E_P}$$

. . . FORMULAS

TRANSFORMER TURNS (E AND I)

$$E_S = \frac{E_P \times T_S}{T_P}$$

$$E_P = \frac{E_S \times T_P}{T_S}$$

$$T_P = \frac{E_P \times T_S}{E_S}$$

$$I_P = \frac{I_S \times T_S}{T_P}$$

$$\frac{I_P}{I_S} = \frac{T_S}{T_P}$$

TRANSFORMER RATIO

$$ratio = \frac{E_P}{E_S}$$

(primary number is shown first)

A/C MOTORS

$$RPM = \frac{F \times 120}{P}$$

$$F = \frac{RPM \times P}{120}$$

$$P = \frac{F \times 120}{RPM}$$

CONVERSIONS

1 inch = 25.4 millimeters
1 inch = 2.54 centimeters
1 foot = .3048 meters
1 millimeter = 0.03937 inch
1 centimeter = 0.3937 inch
1 meter = 3.28084 feet
1 cubic inch = 16.387064 cubic centimeters
1 cubic centimeter = 0.061024 cubic inch
1 square millimeter = 0.001550 square inch
1 square inch = 645.16 square millimeters

POWER/THREE–PHASE

$$P = I \times E \times 1.73 \times PF$$

Note: Do not use 1.73 for single-phase

$$E = \frac{P}{I \times 1.73 \times PF}$$

$$I = \frac{P}{E \times 1.73 \times PF}$$

$$PF = \frac{P}{E \times I \times 1.73}$$

$$kVA = \frac{I_P \times E_P \times 1.73}{1000}$$

$$kVA = \frac{I_S \times E_S \times 1.73}{1000}$$

$$I = \frac{kVA \times 1000}{1.73 \times E \text{ (primary or secondary delta or wye)}}$$

BALANCED THREE–PHASE WYE

Line E = 208 V

Phase E = 120 V

$$I_{line} = I_{phase}$$

$$E_{line} = E_{phase} \times 1.73$$

$$E_{phase} = \frac{E_{line}}{1.73}$$

$$I_{phase} = \frac{VA \, per \, phase}{volts \, per \, phase}$$

BALANCED THREE–PHASE DELTA

Line E = 240 V

Phase E = 240 V

$$I_{phase} = \frac{phase \, VA}{phase \, volts}$$

$$I_{line} = 1.73 \times I_{phase}$$

BALANCED THREE–PHASE DELTA OR WYE

total watts = $1.73 \times E$ line $\times$ I Line

$$\frac{total \, watts}{3} = watts \, per \, phase$$

RESIDENTIAL ELECTRICAL SYMBOLS . . .

LIGHTING OUTLETS

OUTLET BOX AND INCANDESCENT LIGHTING FIXTURE	CEILING WALL
INCANDESCENT TRACK LIGHTING	
BLANKED OUTLET	(B) (B)
DROP CORD	(D)
EXIT LIGHT AND OUTLET BOX. SHADED AREAS DENOTE FACES.	
OUTDOOR POLE-MOUNTED FIXTURES	
JUNCTION BOX	(J) (J)
LAMPHOLDER WITH PULL SWITCH	(L)$_{PS}$ (L)$_{PS}$
MULTIPLE FLOODLIGHT ASSEMBLY	
EMERGENCY BATTERY PACK WITH CHARGER	
INDIVIDUAL FLUORESCENT FIXTURE	
OUTLET BOX AND FLUORESCENT LIGHTING TRACK FIXTURE	
CONTINUOUS FLUORESCENT FIXTURE	
SURFACE-MOUNTED FLUORESCENT FIXTURE	

PANELBOARDS

FLUSH-MOUNTED PANELBOARD AND CABINET	
SURFACE-MOUNTED PANELBOARD AND CABINET	

CONVENIENCE OUTLETS

SINGLE RECEPTACLE OUTLET	
DUPLEX RECEPTACLE OUTLET	
TRIPLEX RECEPTACLE OUTLET	
SPLIT-WIRED DUPLEX RECEPTACLE OUTLET	
SPLIT-WIRED TRIPLEX RECEPTACLE OUTLET	
SINGLE SPECIAL-PURPOSE RECEPTACLE OUTLET	
DUPLEX SPECIAL-PURPOSE RECEPTACLE OUTLET	
RANGE OUTLET	R
SPECIAL-PURPOSE CONNECTION	DW
CLOSED-CIRCUIT TELEVISION CAMERA	
CLOCK HANGER RECEPTACLE	(C)
FAN HANGER RECEPTACLE	(F)
FLOOR SINGLE RECEPTACLE OUTLET	
FLOOR DUPLEX RECEPTACLE OUTLET	
FLOOR SPECIAL-PURPOSE OUTLET	
UNDERFLOOR DUCT AND JUNCTION BOX FOR TRIPLE, DOUBLE, OR SINGLE DUCT SYSTEM AS INDICATED BY NUMBER OF PARALLEL LINES	

BUSDUCTS AND WIREWAYS

SERVICE, FEEDER, OR PLUG-IN BUSWAY	B B B
CABLE THROUGH LADDER OR CHANNEL	C C C
WIREWAY	W W W

SWITCH OUTLETS

SINGLE-POLE SWITCH	S
DOUBLE-POLE SWITCH	S$_2$
THREE-WAY SWITCH	S$_3$
FOUR-WAY SWITCH	S$_4$
AUTOMATIC DOOR SWITCH	S$_D$
KEY-OPERATED SWITCH	S$_K$
CIRCUIT BREAKER	S$_{CB}$
WEATHERPROOF CIRCUIT BREAKER	S$_{WCB}$
DIMMER	S$_{DM}$
REMOTE CONTROL SWITCH	S$_{RC}$
WEATHERPROOF SWITCH	S$_{WP}$
FUSED SWITCH	S$_F$
WEATHERPROOF FUSED SWITCH	S$_{WF}$
TIME SWITCH	S$_T$
CEILING PULL SWITCH	
SWITCH AND SINGLE RECEPTACLE	S
SWITCH AND DOUBLE RECEPTACLE	S
A STANDARD SYMBOL WITH AN ADDED LOWERCASE SUBSCRIPT LETTER IS USED TO DESIGNATE A VARIATION IN STANDARD EQUIPMENT	a,b a,b S$_{a,b}$

... RESIDENTIAL ELECTRICAL SYMBOLS

COMMERCIAL AND INDUSTRIAL SYSTEMS

PAGING SYSTEM DEVICE

FIRE ALARM SYSTEM DEVICE

COMPUTER DATA SYSTEM DEVICE

PRIVATE TELEPHONE SYSTEM DEVICE

SOUND SYSTEM

FIRE ALARM CONTROL PANEL — FACP

SIGNALING SYSTEM OUTLETS FOR RESIDENTIAL SYSTEMS

PUSHBUTTON

BUZZER

BELL

BELL AND BUZZER COMBINATION

COMPUTER DATA OUTLET

BELL RINGING TRANSFORMER — BT

ELECTRIC DOOR OPENER — D

CHIME — CH

TELEVISION OUTLET — TV

THERMOSTAT — T

UNDERGROUND ELECTRICAL DISTRIBUTION OR ELECTRICAL LIGHTING SYSTEMS

MANHOLE — M

HANDHOLE — H

TRANSFORMER-MANHOLE OR VAULT — TM

TRANSFORMER PAD — TP

UNDERGROUND DIRECT BURIAL CABLE

UNDERGROUND DUCT LINE

STREET LIGHT STANDARD FED FROM UNDERGROUND CIRCUIT

ABOVE-GROUND ELECTRICAL DISTRIBUTION OR LIGHTING SYSTEMS

POLE

STREET LIGHT AND BRACKET

PRIMARY CIRCUIT

SECONDARY CIRCUIT

DOWN GUY

HEAD GUY

SIDEWALK GUY

SERVICE WEATHERHEAD

PANEL CIRCUITS AND MISCELLANEOUS

LIGHTING PANEL

POWER PANEL

WIRING – CONCEALED IN CEILING OR WALL

WIRING – CONCEALED IN FLOOR

WIRING EXPOSED

HOME RUN TO PANEL BOARD
Indicate number of circuits by number of arrows. Any circuit without such designation indicates a two-wire circuit. For a greater number of wires indicate as follows: —///— (3 wires) —////— (4 wires), etc.

FEEDERS
Use heavy lines and designate by number corresponding to listing in feeder schedule

WIRING TURNED UP

WIRING TURNED DOWN

GENERATOR — G

MOTOR — M

INSTRUMENT (SPECIFY) — I

TRANSFORMER — T

CONTROLLER

EXTERNALLY-OPERATED DISCONNECT SWITCH

PULL BOX

ABBREVIATIONS . . .

A

abbreviation	ABBR
acoustic	ACST
acoustical tile	ACT. or AT.
adhesive	ADD. or ADH
adjustable	ADJ
adjustable-trip circuit breaker	ATCB
aggregate	AGGR
aileron	AIL
air conditioner	A/C
air handler	A/H
air tight	AT
alarm	ALM
alloy	ALY
alternating current	AC
aluminum	Al
ambient	AMB
Ambulatory Health Care Center	AHCC
American National Standards Institute	ANSI
American Wire Gauge	AWG
ammeter	A or AM
ampere	A or AMP
ampere interrupting rating	AIR.
amps	A
anchor bolt	AB
anode	A
antenna	ANT.
apartment	APT
appliance	APPL
approved	APPD or APVD
approximate	APPROX
approximately	APPROX
architectural	ARCH.
architecture	ARCH.
area	A
area drain	AD
armature	A or ARM.
asphalt	ASPH
asphalt tile	AT.
as required	AR
Assured Equipment Grounding Program	AEGP
astragal	A
Authority Having Jurisdiction	AHJ
automatic	AU or AUTO
automatic sprinkler	AS
auxiliary	AUX
avenue	AVE
azimuth	AZ

B

basement	BSMT
bathroom	B
bathtub	BT
battery (electric)	BAT.
beam	BM
bearing	BRG
bearing plate	BPL or BRG PL
bedroom	BR
benchmark	BM
black	BK
block	BLK
blocking	BLKG
blue	BL
board	BD
board foot	BF
bonding jumper	BJ
boulevard	BLVD
brake relay	BR
brass	BRS
brick	BRK

bridge	BRDG
bronze	BRZ
brown	BR
building	BL or BLDG
building line	BL
built-up roofing	BUR
bypass	BYP

C

cabinet	CAB.
cable	CA
Cable Antenna Television	CATV
cantilever	CANTIL
capacitor	CAP.
cased opening	CO
casement	CSMT
casing	CSG
cast iron	CI
cast-iron pipe	CIP
cast steel	CS
cast stone	CS or CST
catch basin	CB
cathode	K
ceiling	CLG
cellar	CEL
Celsius	°C
cement	CEM
cement floor	CF
center	CTR
centerline	CL
center-to-center	C to C
centigrade	C
central processing unit	CPU
ceramic	CER
ceramic tile	CT
ceramic-tile floor	CTF
channel	CHAN
chapter	CH
chimney	CHM
circuit	CIR or CKT
circuit breaker	CB
circuit interrupter	CI
circular mils	CM
cleanout	CO
clockwise	CW
closet	CLO
coarse	CRS
coated	CTD
coaxial	COAX
Code-Making Panel	CMP
cold air	CA
cold water	CW
column	COL
compacted	COMP
concrete	CONC
concrete block	CCB or CONC BLK
concrete floor	CCF
concrete pipe	CP
condenser	COND
conductor resistivity	K
conduit	C or CND
construction joint	CJ
continuous	CONT
contour	CTR
control	CONT
control joint	CJ or CLJ
control relay	CR
control relay master	CRM
copper	Cu
corner	COR
cornice	COR

corrugated	CORR
counterclockwise	CCW
counter electromotive force	CEMF
county	CO
cubic	CU
cubic foot	CU FT
cubic foot per minute	CFM
cubic foot per second	CFS
cubic inch	CU IN.
cubic yard	CU YD
current	I
current transformer	CT
cut out	CO
cycles per second	CPS

D

damper	DMPR
dampproofing	DP
dead load	DL
decibel	DB
deck	DK
demolition	DML
depth	DP
detail	DET or DTL
diagonal	DIAG
diagram	DIAG
diameter	D or DIA
dimension	DIM.
dimmer	DMR
dining room	DR
diode	DIO
direct current	DC
disconnect switch	DS
dishwasher	DW
distribution	DISTR
distribution panel	DPNL
division	DIV
door	DR
dormer	DRM
double-acting	DBL ACT
double hung window	DHW
double-pole	DP
double-pole double-throw	DPDT
double-pole double-throw switch	DPDT SW
double-pole single-throw	DPST
double-pole single-throw switch	DPST SW
double-pole switch	DP SW
double strength glass	DSG
double-throw	DT
down	D or DN
downspout	DS
drain	DR
drain tile	DT
drawing	DWG
drinking fountain	DF
drum switch	DS
dryer	D
drywall	DW
duplex	DX
dust tight	DT
dutch door	DD
duty cycle	DTY CY
dynamic braking contactor or relay	DB

E

each	EA
east	E
efficiency	Eff
ejector pump	EP
electric	ELEC

...ABBREVIATIONS...

electrical	ELEC
electrical metallic tubing	EMT
electric panel	EP
electromechanical	ELMCH
electromotive force	EMF
electronic	ELEK
elevation	EL
elevator	ELEV
enamel	ENAM
entrance	ENTR
equipment	EQPT
equipment bonding jumper	EBJ
equipment grounding conductor	EGC
equivalent	EQUIV
estimate	EST
excavate	EXC
exception	Ex.
exhaust	EXH
existing	EXIST. or EXST
expanded metal	EM
expansion joint	EXP JT
explosionproof	EP
exterior	EXT
exterior grade	EXT GR

F

face brick	FB
Fahrenheit	°F
fast	F
field	F
figure	FIG.
fine print note	FPN
finish	FNSH
finish all over	FAO
finished floor	FNSH FL
finished grade	FG or FIN GR
finish one side	F1S
finish two sides	F2S
firebrick	FBCK
fire door	FDR
fire extinguisher	FEXT
fire hydrant	FHY
fireplace	FP
fireproof	FPRF
fire wall	FW
fixed window	FX WDW
fixture	FXTR
flammable	FLMB
flashing	FL
flat	FL
flexible metallic conduit	FMC
float switch	FS
floor	FL
floor drain	FD
flooring	FLG or FLR
floor line	FL
flow switch	FLS
fluorescent	FLUOR or FLUR
flush	FL
flush mount	FLMT
footing	FTG
foot per minute	FPM
foot per second	FPS
foot switch	FTS
forward	F or FWD
foundation	FDN
four-pole	4P
four-pole double-throw switch	4PDT SW
four-pole single-throw switch	4PST SW
four-pole switch	4PSW
frame	FR

frequency	FREQ
front view	FV
full-load amps	FLA
full-load current	FLC
full-load torque	FLT
furnace	FUR.
furring	FUR.
fuse	FU
fuse block	FB
fuse box	FUBX
fuse holder	FUHLR
fusible	FSBL
future	FUT

G

gallon per hour	GPH
gallon per minute	GPM
galvanized	GALV
garage	GAR
gas	G
gate	G
gauge	GA
generator	GEN
glass	GL or GLS
glass block	GLB
glaze	GLZ
gold	Au
grade	GR
grade line	GL
gravel	GVL
gray	GY
green	G or GR
gross vehicle weight	GVW
ground	G, GND, GRD, or GRND
grounded (outlet)	G
ground-fault circuit interrupter	GFCI
ground fault protection of equipment	GFPE
grounding electrode conductor	GEC
grounding electrode system	GES
gypsum	GYP
gypsum sheathing board	GSB

H

hand-off-auto	HOA
handrail	HNDRL
hardboard	HBD
hardware	HDW
hardwood	HDWD
hazardous	HAZ
header	HDR
heating	HTG
heating, air-conditioning, refrigeration	HACR
heating, ventilating, and air conditioning	HVAC
heavy-duty	HD
hertz	Hz
highway	HWY
hollow core	HC
hollow metal door	HMD
horizontal	HOR
horsepower	HP
hose bibb	HB
hot water	HW
hot water heater	HWH
hours	HRS
hydraulic	HYDR

I

immersion detection circuit interrupter	IDCI

inch	IN.
inch per second	IPS
inch-pound	IN. LB
infrared	IR
inside diameter	ID
instantaneous overload	IOL
instantaneous-trip circuit breaker	ITB
insulation	INSUL
integrated circuit	IC
interior	INT or INTR
interlock	INTLK
intermediate	INT
intermediate metal conduit	IMC
International Electrotechnical Commission	IEC
interrupt	INT
inverse time breaker	ITB
inverse-time circuit breaker	ITCB
iron	I
iron pipe	IP
isolated ground	IG

J

jamb	JB or JMB
joint	JT
joist	J or JST
junction	JCT
junction box	JB

K

key way	KWY
kick plate	KPL
kiln-dried	KD
kilo (1000)	k
1000 circular mils	kcmil
1000'	kFT
kilovolt amps	kVA
kilowatt	kW
kilowatt-hour	kWh
kitchen	K or KIT.
knife switch	KN SW
knockout	KO

L

lamp	LT
lath	LTH
laundry	LAU
laundry tray	LT
lavatory	LAV
left	L
left hand	LH
less-flammable, liquid-insulated	LFLI
library	LBRY or LIB
light	LT
lighting	LTG
lighting panel	LP
lights	LTS
limit switch	LS
line	L
linoleum	LINO or LINOL
lintel	LNTL
live load	LL
living room	LR
load	L
location	LOC
locked-rotor ampacity	LRA
locked-rotor current	LRC
louver	LVR or LV
lumber	LBR

... ABBREVIATIONS ...

M

magnetic brake	MB
main	MN
main bonding jumper	MBJ
main control center	MCC
manhole	MH
manual	MAN., MN, or MNL
manufacturer	MFR
marble	MRB
masonry	MSNRY
masonry opening	MO
material	MATL or MTL
maximum	MAX
maximum working pressure	MWP
mechanical	MECH
medicine cabinet	MC
medium	MED
memory	MEM
metal	MET or MTL
metal anchor	MA
metal door	METD
metal flashing	METF
metal jalousie	METJ
metal lath and plaster	MLP
metal threshold	MT
mezzanine	MEZZ
miles per gallon	MPG
miles per hour	MPH
minimum	MIN
mirror	MIR
miscellaneous	MISC
molding	MLDG
monolithic	ML
mortar	MOR
motor	M, MOT, or MTR
motor branch-circuit, short-circuit, ground-fault	MBCSCGF
motor circuit switch	MCS
motor control center	MCC
motor starter	M
motor switch	MS
mounted	MTD

N

nameplate	NPL
National Electrical Code®	NEC®
National Electrical Manufacturers Association	NEMA
National Electrical Safety Code	NESC
National Fire Protection Association	NFPA
negative	NEG
net weight	NTWT
neutral	N or NEUT
nominal	NOM
nonadjustable-trip circuit breaker	NATCB
non-time delay fuse	NTDF
normally closed	NC
normally open	NO
north	N
nosing	NOS
not to scale	NTS
number	NO.

O

Occupational Safety and Health Administration	OSHA
ohmmeter	OHM.
on center	OC
opaque	OPA

opening	OPNG
open web joist	OJ or OWJ
orange	O
ounces per inch	OZ/IN.
outlet	OUT.
outside diameter	OD
overall	OA
overcurrent	OC
overcurrent protection device	OCPD
overhang	OVHG
overhead	OH.
overload	OL
overload relay	OL

P

paint	PNT
painted	PTD
pair	PR
panel	PNL
pantry	PAN.
parallel	PRL
peak-to-peak	P-P
perpendicular	PERP
personal computer	PC
phase	PH
piece	PC
piling	PLG
pillar	PLR
pilot light	PL
piping	PP
pitch	P
plank	PLK
plaster	PLAS
plastic	PLSTC
plate	PL
plate glass	PLGL
plugging switch	PLS
plumbing	PLMB or PLBG
plywood	PLYWD
pneumatic	PNEU
point of beginning	POB
pole	P
polyvinyl chloride	PVC
porcelain	PORC
porch	P
positive	POS
pound(s)	LB
pounds per feet	LB-FT
pounds per inch	LB-IN.
pounds per square foot	PSF
pounds per square inch	PSI
power	P or PWR
power consumed	P
power factor	PF
precast	PRCST
prefabricated	PFB or PREFAB
prefinished	PFN
pressure switch	PS
primary switch	PRI
property line	PL
pull box	PB
pull switch	PS
pull-up torque	PUT
pushbutton	PB

Q

quadrant	QDRNT
quantity	QTY
quarry tile	QT

quarry-tile roof	QTR
quart	QT
quick-acting	QA

R

radius	R
raintight	RT
random	RDM or RNDM
range	R or RNG
receipt of comments	ROC
receipt of proposals	ROP
receptacle	RECEPT or RCPT
recess	REC
recessed	REC
rectifier	REC
red	R
reference	REF
refrigerator	REF
register	REG or RGTR
reinforce	RE
reinforced concrete	RC
reinforcing steel	RST
reinforcing steel bar	REBAR
required	REQD
resistance	R
resistor	R or RES
return	RTN
reverse	R or REV
reverse-acting	RACT
revision	REV
revolutions per minute	RPM
revolutions per second	RPS
rheostat	RH
ribbed	RIB
right	R
right hand	RH
rigid	RGD
riser	R
road	RD
roll roofing	RR
roof	RF
roof drain	RD
roofing	RFG
room	R or RM
root mean square	RMS
rotor	RTR
rough	RGH
rough opening	RO
rough sawn	RS

S

safety switch	SSW
sanitary	SAN
scale	SC
schedule	SCH or SCHED
screen	SCR
scuttle	S
secondary	SEC
section	SECT
selector switch	SS
series	S
service	SERV
service entrance	SE
service factor	SF
sewer	SEW.
shake	SHK
sheathing	SHTHG
sheet	SH or SHT
sheet metal	SM
shelf and rod	SH & RD

. . . ABBREVIATIONS

shelving	SHELV
shingle	SHGL
shower	SH
shutter	SHTR
siding	SDG
silicon controlled rectifier	SCR
sill cock	SC
silver	Ag
single-phase	1PH
single-pole	SP
single-pole circuit breaker	SPCB
single-pole double-throw	SPDT
single-pole double-throw switch	SPDT SW
single-pole single-throw	SPST
single-pole single-throw switch	SPST SW
single-pole switch	SP SW
single strength glass	SSG
sink	S or SK
skylight	SLT
slate	S, SL, or SLT
sliding door	SLD
slope	SLP
slow	S
smoke detector	SD
socket	SOC
soffit	SF
soil pipe	SP
solenoid	SOL
solid core	SC
south	S
spare	SP
specification	SPEC
splash block	SB
square	SQ
square foot	SQ FT
square inch	SQ IN.
square yard	SQ YD
stack	STK
stainless steel	SST
stairs	ST
standard	STD
standpipe	SP
starter	START or STR
steel	STL
stone	STN
storage	STOR
street	ST
structural glass	SG
sump pump	SP
supply	SPLY
surface four sides	S4S
surface one side	S1S
switch	S or SW
switched disconnect	SWD

T

telephone	TEL
television	TV
temperature	TEMP
tempered	TEMP
terazzo	TER
terminal	T or TERM.
terminal board	TB
terra cotta	TC
thermal	THRM
thermally protected	TP
thermostat	THERMO
thermostat switch	THS
three-phase	3PH
three-pole	3P
three-pole double-throw	3PDT
three-pole single-throw	3PST
three-way	3WAY
three-wire	3W
threshold	TH
time	T
time delay	TD
time-delay fuse	TDF
time delay relay	TR
toilet	T
tongue-and-groove	T & G
torque	T
transformer	T, TRANS, or XFMR
transformer, primary side	H
transformer, secondary side	X
tread	TR
triple-pole double-throw	3PDT
triple-pole double-throw switch	3PDT SW
triple-pole single-throw	3PST
triple-pole single-throw switch	3PST SW
triple-pole switch	3P SW
truss	TR
two-phase	2PH
two-pole	DP
two-pole double-throw	DPDT
two-pole single-throw	DPST
typical	TYP

U

unclamp	UCL
underground	UGND
underground feeder	UF
undervoltage	UV
Underwriters Laboratories Inc.	UL
unexcavated	UNEXC
unfinished	UNFIN
up	U
utility room	U RM

V

valley	VAL
valve	V
vapor seal	VS
vaportight	VT
vent	V
ventilation	VENT.
vent pipe	VP
vent stack	VS
vertical	V or VERT
vinyl tile	VTILE or VT
violet	V
volt	V
voltage	E or V
voltage drop	VD
volt amps	VA
volts	V
volts alternating current	VAC
volts direct current	VDC
volume	VOL

W

wainscot	WAIN
walk-in closet	WIC
warm air	WA
washing machine	WM
waste pipe	WP
waste stack	WS
water	WTR
water closet	WC
water heater	WH
water meter	WM
waterproof	WP
watt(s)	W
weatherproof	WP
welded	WLD
welded wire fabric	WWF
west	W
white	W
wide flange	WF
wire gauge	WG
wire mesh	WM
with	W/
without	W/O
wood	WD
wrought iron	WI

Y

yellow	Y

UNITS OF ENERGY

Energy	Btu	ft-lb	J	kcal	kWh
British thermal unit	1	777.9	1.056	0.252	2.930×10^{-4}
Foot-pound	1.285×10^{-3}	1	1.356	3.240×10^{-4}	3.766×10^{-7}
Joule	9.481×10^{-4}	0.7376	1	2.390×10^{-4}	2.778×10^{-7}
Kilocalorie	3.968	3.086	4.184	1	1.163×10^{-3}
Kilowatt-hour	3.413	2.655×10^{6}	3.6×10^{6}	860.2	1

VOLTAGE CONVERSIONS

To Convert	To	Multiply By
rms	Average	.9
rms	Peak	1.414
Average	rms	1.111
Average	Peak	1.567
Peak	rms	.707
Peak	Average	.637
Peak	Peak-to-peak	2

DECIMAL EQUIVALENTS OF AN INCH

Fraction	Decimal	Fraction	Decimal	Fraction	Decimal	Fraction	Decimal
1/64	0.015625	17/64	0.265625	33/64	0.515625	49/64	0.765625
1/32	0.03125	9/32	0.28125	17/32	0.53125	25/32	0.78125
3/64	0.046875	19/64	0.296875	35/64	0.546875	51/64	0.796875
1/16	0.0625	5/16	0.3125	9/16	0.5625	13/16	0.8125
5/64	0.078125	21/64	0.328125	37/64	0.578125	53/64	0.828125
3/32	0.09375	11/32	0.34375	19/32	0.59375	27/32	0.84375
7/64	0.109375	23/64	0.359375	39/64	0.609375	55/64	0.859375
1/8	0.125	3/8	0.375	5/8	0.625	7/8	0.875
9/64	0.140625	25/64	0.390625	41/64	0.640625	57/64	0.890625
5/32	0.15625	13/32	0.40625	21/32	0.65625	29/32	0.90625
11/64	0.171875	27/64	0.421875	43/64	0.671875	59/64	0.921875
3/16	0.1875	7/16	0.4375	11/16	0.6875	15/16	0.9375
13/64	0.203125	29/64	0.453125	45/64	0.703125	61/64	0.953125
7/32	0.21875	15/32	0.46875	23/32	0.71875	31/32	0.96875
15/64	0.234375	31/64	0.484375	47/64	0.734375	63/64	0.984375
1/4	0.250	1/2	0.500	3/4	0.750	1	1.000

RACEWAYS

EMT	Electrical Metallic Tubing
ENT	Electrical Nonmetallic Tubing
FMC	Flexible Metal Conduit
FMT	Flexible Metallic Tubing
IMC	Intermediate Metal Conduit
LFMC	Liquidtight Flexible Metal Conduit
LFNC	Liquidtight Flexible Nonmetallic Conduit
RMC	Rigid Metal Conduit
RNC	Rigid Nonmetallic Conduit

COMMON ELECTRICAL INSULATIONS

60°C 140°F	75°C 167°F	90°C 194°F
TW	FEPW	TBS
UF	RH	SA
	RHW	SIS
	THHW	FEP
	THW	FEPB
	THWN	MI
	XHHW	RHH
	USE	RHW-2
	ZW	THHN
		THHW
		THW-2
		THWN-2
		USE-2
		XHH
		XHHW
		XHHW-2
		ZW-2

INSULATION
• TABLE 310.13

AMPACITY
• TABLE 310.16

COPPER, ALUMINUM, OR COPPER-CLAD ALUMINUM

CABLES

AC	Armored Cable
BX	Tradename for AC
FCC	Flat Conductor Cable
IGS	Integrated Gas Spacer Cable
MC	Metal-Clad Cable
MI	Mineral-Insulated, Metal Sheathed Cable
MV	Medium Voltage
NM	Nonmetallic-Sheathed Cable (dry)
NMC	Nonmetallic-Sheathed Cable (dry or damp)
NMS	Nonmetallic-Sheathed Cable (dry)
SE	Service-Entrance Cable (dry)
TC	Tray Cable
UF	Underground Feeder Cable
USE	Underground Service-Entrance Cable

FUSES AND ITCBs

Increase	Standard Ampere Ratings
5	15, 20, 25, 30, 35, 40, 45
10	50, 60, 70, 80, 90, 100, 110
25	125, 150, 175, 200, 225
50	250, 300, 350, 400, 450
100	500, 600, 700, 800
200	1000, 1200
400	1600, 2000
500	2500
1000	3000, 4000, 5000, 6000

1 A, 3 A, 6 A, 10 A, and 601 A are additional standard ratings for fuses.

MOTOR TORQUE

Torque	Starting Torque	Nominal Torque Rating
$T = \dfrac{HP \times 5252}{rpm}$ where T = torque HP = horsepower 5252 = constant $\left(\dfrac{33,000 \text{ lb-ft}}{\pi \times 2} = 5252\right)$ rpm = revolutions per minute	$T = \dfrac{HP \times 5252}{rpm} \times \%$ where HP = horsepower 5252 = constant $\left(\dfrac{33,000 \text{ lb-ft}}{\pi \times 2} = 5252\right)$ rpm = revolutions per minute % = motor class percentage	$T = \dfrac{HP \times 63,000}{rpm}$ where T = nominal torque rating (in lb-in) 63,000 = constant HP = horsepower rpm = revolutions per minute

HAZARDOUS LOCATIONS			
Class	**Division**	**Group**	**Material**
I	1 or 2	A	Acetylene
	1 or 2	B	Hydrogen, butadiene, ethylene oxide, propylene oxide
	1 or 2	C	Carbon monoxide, ether, ethylene, hydrogen sulfide, morpholine, cyclopropane
	1 or 2	D	Gasoline, benzene, butane, propane, alcohol, acetone, ammonia, vinyl chloride
II	1 or 2	E	Metal dusts
	1 or 2	F	Carbon black, coke dust, coal
	1 or 2	G	Grain dust, flour, starch, sugar, plastics
III	1 or 2	No groups	Wood chips, cotton, flax, nylon

A

accessible: A description for equipment that admits close approach and is not guarded by locked doors, elevation, etc.

adjustable-trip CBs (ATCBs): CBs (circuit breakers) whose trip setting can be changed by adjusting the ampere setpoint, trip time characteristics, or both, within a particular range.

alternating current (AC): Current that reverses its direction of flow at regular intervals. See *current*.

ambient temperature: The temperature of air around a conductor or a piece of equipment.

ampacity: The current that a conductor can carry continuously, under the conditions of use.

apparent power: The product of voltage and current in a circuit calculated without considering the phase shift that may be present between total voltage and current in the circuit. See *voltage* and *current*.

appliance: Any utilization equipment that performs one or more functions, such as clothes washing, air conditioning, cooking, etc.

appliance branch circuit: A branch circuit that supplies energy to one or more outlets to which appliances are to be connected.

approved: Acceptable to the authority having jurisdiction (AHJ).

armored cable (AC): A factory assembly that contains conductors within a jacket made of a spiral wrap of steel.

array: An assembly of modules or panels mounted on a support structure to form a direct current, power-producing unit.

askarel: A group of nonflammable synthetic chlorinated hydrocarbons that were once used where nonflammable insulating oils were required.

autotransformers: Single-winding transformers that share a common winding between the primary and secondary circuits.

auxiliary gutter: A sheet-metal enclosure equipped with hinged or removable covers that is used to supplement wiring space.

B

bare conductor: A conductor with no insulation or covering of any type.

bathroom: An area with a basin and one or more of a toilet, tub, or shower.

bend: Any change in direction of a raceway.

bonding: Joining metal parts to form a continuous path to safely conduct any current that is commonly imposed.

box: A metallic or nonmetallic electrical enclosure used for equipment, devices, and pulling or terminating conductors.

branch-circuit: The portion of the electrical circuit between the last overcurrent device (fuse or circuit breaker) and the outlets or utilization equipment.

branch-circuit conductor: The circuit conductor(s) between the final overcurrent device protecting the circuit and the outlet(s).

branch-circuit rating: The ampere rating or setting of the overcurrent device protecting the conductors.

building: A stand-alone structure or a structure that is separated from adjoining structures by fire division walls.

bulk storage plant: A location where liquids are received by tank vessels, pipelines, or tank cars, and are stored or blended in bulk for the purpose of distribution to similar vehicles or containers.

bushing: A fitting placed on the end of a conduit to protect the conductor's insulation from abrasion.

busway: A sheet metal enclosure that contains factory-assembled aluminum or copper busbars that are supported on insulators.

C

cable: A factory assembly with two or more conductors and an overall covering.

cable assembly: A flexible assembly containing multi-conductors with a protective outer sheath.

cablebus: An assembly of insulated conductors and terminations in an enclosed, ventilated protective metal housing.

cable tray system (CTS): An assembly of sections and associated fittings that form a rigid structural system used to support cables and raceways.

capacitance: The property of an electrical device that permits the storage of electrically separated charges when potential differences exist between the conductors. See *device*.

cartridge fuse: A fuse constructed of a metallic link or links that are designed to open at predetermined current levels to protect circuit conductors and equipment.

cell: A single, enclosed, tubular space in a precast cellular concrete slab floor with the direction of the cell being parallel to the direction of the floor member.

cellular metal floor raceway: The hollow spaces of cellular metal floors, with fittings, approved as enclosures for electric conductors.

circuit: A complete path through which electricity flows.

circuit breaker (CB): A device that opens and closes circuits by nonautomatic means and opens circuits automatically when a predetermined overcurrent exists.

circular mil: A measurement used to determine the cross-sectional area of a conductor.

Class I location: A hazardous location in which sufficient quantities of flammable gases and vapors are present in the air to cause an explosion or ignite the hazardous materials.

Class II location: A hazardous location in which sufficient quantities of combustible dust are present in the air to cause an explosion or ignite the hazardous materials.

Class III location: A hazardous location in which easily-ignitable fibers or flyings are present in the air, but not in a sufficient quantity to cause an explosion or ignite the hazardous materials.

compact conductor: A conductor that has been compressed to eliminate voids between strands.

conductor: A slender rod or wire that is used to control the flow of electrons in an electrical circuit.

conduit body: A conduit fitting that provides access to the raceway system through a removable cover at a junction or termination point.

conduit seal: A fitting that is inserted into runs of conduit to isolate certain electrical apparatus from atmospheric hazards.

continuous load: A load in which the maximum current may continue for three hours or more.

controller: The device in a motor circuit that turns the motor ON or OFF.

cover: The shortest distance measured between a point on the top surface of any direct-buried conductor, cable, conduit, or other raceway and the top surface of finished grade, concrete, or similar cover.

covered conductor: A conductor not encased in a material recognized by the NEC®.

current: The amount of electrons flowing through an electrical circuit.

current-limiting fuses: Fuses that open a circuit in less than one-half of a cycle to protect the circuit components from damaging short-circuit currents.

current transformer: A transformer that creates a constant ratio of primary to secondary current instead of attempting to maintain a constant ratio of primary to secondary voltage.

D

damp location: A partially protected area subject to some moisture.

dead front: A cover required for the operation of a plug or connector.

demand: The amount of electricity required at a given time.

demand factor: The ratio of the maximum demand of a system, or part of a system, to the total connected load of a system, or to the part of the system under consideration.

devices: Electrical components, such as receptacles and switches, that are designed to carry, but not utilize, electricity.

device box: A box that houses an electrical device.

direct current (DC): Current that flows in one direction. See *current*.

disconnecting means: A device, or group of devices, by which the circuit conductors are disconnected from their source of supply.

division: The classification assigned to each Class based upon the likelihood of the presence of the hazardous substance in the atmosphere.

Division 1 location: A hazardous location in which the hazardous substance is normally present in the air in sufficient quantities to cause an explosion or ignite the hazardous materials.

Division 2 location: A hazardous location in which the hazardous substance is not normally present in the air in sufficient quantities to cause an explosion or ignite the hazardous materials.

dry location: A location that is not normally damp or wet.

dry-niche lighting fixture: A lighting fixture installed in the pool wall in a niche sealed against pool water entry.

dry-type transformer: A transformer that provides air circulation based on the principle of heat transfer.

dust-ignitionproof: Enclosed in a manner that prevents the entrance of dust and does not permit arcs, sparks, or excessive temperature to cause ignition of exterior accumulations of specified dust.

dustproof: Construction in which dust does not interfere with the successful operation of equipment.

dusttight: Construction that does not permit dust to enter the enclosing case under specified test conditions.

dwelling: A structure that contains eating, living, and sleeping space, and permanent provisions for cooking and sanitation.

dwelling unit: A single unit for one or more persons that includes permanent provisions for living, sleeping, cooking, and sanitation.

dynamic load: A load that produces a small but constant vibration.

E

eddy current: An unwanted, induced current in the core of a transformer.

Edison-base fuse: A plug fuse that incorporates a screw configuration that is interchangeable with fuses or other ampere ratings.

effectively grounded: Grounded with sufficient low impedance and current-carrying capacity to prevent hazardous voltage buildups.

efficiency: The output of a motor divided by the input. See *output* and *input*.

electrical metallic tubing (EMT): A lightweight tubular steel raceway without threads on the ends.

electrical nonmetallic tubing (ENT): A nonmetallic corrugated raceway.

electric-discharge lighting fixture: A lighting fixture that utilizes a ballast for the operation of the lamp.

electric-discharge luminaire: A luminaire that utilizes a ballast for the operation of the lamp.

electron: An elementary particle containing the smallest negative charge.

enclosure: The case or housing of equipment or other apparatus that provides protection from live or energized parts.

energized: Being electrically connected to voltage or being a source of voltage.

energy: The capacity to do work. Usable power.

equipment: Any device, fixture, apparatus, appliance, etc. used in conjunction with electrical installations.

equipment bonding jumper (EBJ): A conductor that connects two or more parts of the EGC.

equipment grounding conductor (EGC): An electrical conductor that provides a low-impedance path between electrical equipment and enclosures and the system grounded conductor and grounding electrode conductor (GEC).

equipotential plane: An area in which all conductive elements are bonded or otherwise connected together in a manner that prevents a difference of potential from developing within the plane.

explosionproof apparatus: Equipment that is enclosed in a case capable of withstanding any explosion that may occur within it, and prevents the ignition of flammable gases or vapors on the outside of the enclosure.

exposed: As applied to wiring methods, a means on a surface or behind panels that allows access.

F

FCC System: A complete wiring system (including FCC, connectors, terminators, adapters, boxes, and receptacles) designed for installation under carpet squares.

feeder: All circuit conductors between the service equipment, the source of a separately derived system, or other supply source, and the final branch-circuit overcurrent device.

feeder neutral load: The maximum unbalance between any of the ungrounded conductors and the grounded conductor.

fire point: The lowest temperature at which a material can give off vapors fast enough to support continuous combustion.

fitting: An electrical system accessory that performs a mechanical function.

flash point (fire point): The temperature at which liquids give off vapor sufficient to form an ignitable mixture with the air near the surface of the liquid.

flat conductor cable (FCC): A cable with three or more flat copper conductors edge-to-edge and separated and enclosed by an insulating material.

flexible cable: An assembly of one or more insulated conductors, with or without braids, contained within an overall outer covering and used for the connection of equipment to a power source.

flexible cord: An assembly of two or more insulated conductors, with or without braids, contained within an overall outer covering and used for the connection of equipment to a power source.

flexible metal conduit (FMC): A raceway of metal strips that are formed into a circular cross-sectional raceway.

forming shell: A structure mounted in a pool and designed to support a wet-niche lighting fixture assembly.

fuse: An overcurrent protection device with a fusible link that melts and opens the circuit when an overload condition or short circuit occurs.

G

general-purpose branch circuit: A branch circuit that supplies two or more outlets for lighting and appliances.

general-use snap switch: A form of general-use switch constructed so that it can be installed in device boxes and similar equipment.

general-use switch: A switch for use in general distribution and branch circuits. The ampere-rated switch is capable of interrupting its rated current at its rated voltage.

generator: A device that is used to convert mechanical power to electrical power.

grade: The level or elevation of the earth on a job site.

ground: A conducting connection between electrical circuits or equipment and the earth.

grounded: Connected to the earth or a conducting body connected to the earth.

grounded conductor: A conductor that has been intentionally grounded.

ground fault: An unintentional connection between an ungrounded conductor and any grounded raceway, box, enclosure, fitting, etc.

ground-fault circuit interrupter receptacles: Devices that interrupt the flow of current to the load when a ground fault occurs that exceeds a predetermined value of current.

grounding conductor: The conductor that connects electrical equipment or the grounded conductor to the grounding electrode.

grounding electrode conductor (GEC): The conductor that connects the grounding electrode(s) to the grounded conductor and/or the equipment grounding conductor (EGC).

grounding receptacles: Receptacles that include a grounding terminal connected to a grounding slot in the receptacle configuration.

H

hazardous location: A location where there is an increased risk of fire or explosion due to the presence of flammable gases, vapors, liquids, combustible dusts, or easily-ignitable fibers or flyings.

header: A transverse metal raceway for electric conductors with access to predetermined cells, permitting the installation of electric conductors from a distribution center to the floor cells.

health care facility: Either a building or a portion of a building that contains occupancies such as hospitals, nursing homes, limited or supervisory care facilities, clinics, medical and dental offices, and either movable or permanent ambulatory facilities.

heating panel: A complete assembly with a junction box or a length of flexible conduit for connection.

heating panel set: A rigid or nonrigid assembly with nonheating leads or a terminal junction suitable for connection.

heating system: A complete system of components such as heating elements, fasteners, nonheating circuit wiring, leads, temperature controllers, safety signs, junction boxes, raceways, and fittings.

hermetic refrigerant motor-compressor: A combination of a compressor and motor enclosed in the same housing, having no external shaft or shaft seals, with the motor operating in the refrigerant.

high-density polyethylene conduit (Type HDPE conduit): Conduit constructed of high-density polyethylene that is resistant to moisture and chemical atmospheres.

high-intensity discharge (HID) lighting fixture: A lighting fixture that generates light from an arc lamp contained within an outer tube.

hospital-grade receptacles: The highest grade receptacles manufactured for the electrical industry.

house load: An electrical load that is metered separately and supplies common usage areas.

hysteresis: A lagging in values resulting in a changing magnetization in a magnetic material.

I

identified: Recognized as suitable for the use, purpose, etc.

immersion detection circuit interrupter (IDCI): Circuit interrupter designed to provide protection against shock when appliances fall into a sink or bathtub.

impedance: The total opposition to the flow of current in a circuit.

impedance heating system: A system in which heat is generated by pipe(s) and rod(s) via an electrical source.

indicating device: A pilot light, buzzer, horn, or other type of alarm. Often, the wiring of a motor control circuit is very elaborate and requires ten times the amount of wiring as the motor power circuit.

individual branch circuit: A branch circuit that supplies only one piece of utilization equipment.

inductance: The property of a circuit that causes it to oppose a change in current due to energy stored in a magnetic field. See *circuit* and *current*.

instantaneous-trip CBs (ITBs): CBs (circuit breakers) with no delay between the fault or overload sensing element and the tripping action of the device.

instrument transformer: A transformer used to reduce higher voltage and current ratings to safer and more suitable levels for the purposes of control and measurement.

insulated conductor: A conductor covered with a material classified as electrical insulation.

insulators: Materials through which current cannot flow easily. See *current*.

interactive system: A system that operates in parallel with, and is permitted to deliver power to, a normal utility service connected to the same load.

intermediate metal conduit (IMC): A raceway of circular cross-section designed for protection and routing of conductors.

intermittent load: A load in which the maximum current does not continue for three hours.

interrupting rating: The maximum amount of current that an OCPD (overcurrent protection device) can clear safely.

intrinsically safe system: A system with an assembly of intrinsically safe apparatus and associated apparatus, which is interconnected and used in hazardous locations to supply equipment.

inverse: Opposite in order.

inverse-time CBs (ITCBs): CBs (circuit breakers) with an intentional delay between the time when the fault or overload is sensed and the time when the CB operates.

inverter: Equipment used to change the voltage level or waveform, or both, of electrical energy.

isolated-ground receptacles: Receptacles in which the grounding terminal is isolated from the device yoke or strap.

isolating switch: A switch designed to isolate an electric circuit from the power source. It has no interrupting rating and is operated only after the circuit has been opened by other means.

isolation transformer: A transformer that utilizes a shield between the primary and secondary windings and a transformer ratio of 1:1 to ensure that the load is separated from the power source.

J

junction box: A box in which splices, taps, or terminations are made.

K

K factor: The resistivity of a conductor based on one mil-foot of wire at a set temperature. See *conductor, resistance,* and *temperature*.

kick: A single bend in a raceway.

L

labeled: Equipment acceptable to the authority having jurisdiction and to which a label has been attached.

lampholders: Devices designed to accommodate a lamp for the purpose of illumination.

lighting and appliance branch-circuit panelboard: A panelboard with more than 10% of its branch-circuit fuses or circuit breakers rated at 30 A or less (15 A, 20 A, 25 A, or 30 A).

lighting outlet: An outlet intended for the direct connection of a lampholder, a lighting fixture, or pendant cord terminating in a lampholder.

lighting track: An assembly consisting of an energized track and lighting fixture heads that can be positioned in any location along the track.

line surge: A temporary increase in the circuit voltage, system voltage, or current that may occur as a result of fluctuations in the electrical distribution system.

liquid-filled transformer: A transformer that utilizes some form of insulating liquid to immerse the core and windings of the transformer to aid in the removal of heat generated by the transformer windings.

liquidtight flexible metal conduit (LFMC): A raceway of circular cross-section with an outer liquidtight, nonmetallic, and sunlight-resistant jacket over an inner helically-wound metal strip.

liquidtight flexible nonmetallic conduit (LFNC): A raceway of circular cross-section with an outer jacket that is resistant to oil, water, sunlight, corrosion, etc. The inner core varies based on intended use.

listed: Equipment, materials, or services that are included in a list published by an organization acceptable to the authority having jurisdiction.

losses: The difference between a motor's input and output. See *input* and *output*.

luminaire: A complete lighting fixture consisting of the lamp or lamps, reflector, or other parts to distribute the light, lamp guards, and lamp power supply.

M

manufactured building: A building of closed construction, normally factory-made or assembled for installation or assembly and installation on building site. Does not include mobile homes, recreational vehicles, park trailers, or manufactured homes.

medium voltage cable (Type MV cable): A single or multiple copper, aluminum, or copper-clad aluminum conductor cable that is constructed of a solid dielectric insulation rated 2001 V or higher.

metal-clad cable (MC): A factory assembly of one or more conductors with or without fiber-optic members.

metal wireway: A sheet metal trough with a hinged or removable cover that houses and protects wires and cables laid in place after the wireway has been installed.

mil: Measure of length equal to 0.001″.

milliampere (mA): $\frac{1}{1000}$ of an ampere (1000 mA = 1 A).

mineral-insulated, metal sheathed cable (Type MI cable): A factory assembled cable construction that consists of one or more conductors that are insulated with a highly compressed refractory mineral insulation.

mobile home: Transportable factory-assembled structure(s) constructed on a permanent chassis for use as a dwelling. A mobile home is not constructed on a permanent foundation but is connected to the required utilities. The term "mobile home" includes manufactured homes.

module: The smallest complete, environmentally-protected assembly of solar cells, exclusive of tracking, designed to generate DC power under sunlight.

motor branch circuit: The point from the last fuse or circuit breaker in the motor circuit out to the motor.

motor control center (MCC): An assembly of one or more enclosed sections with a common power bus and primarily containing motor control units.

motor control circuit: The circuit of a control apparatus or system, which carries electric signals directing the performance of the controller, but does not carry the main power current.

multifamily dwelling: A dwelling with three or more dwelling units.

multioutlet assembly: A surface, flush, or freestanding raceway that contains conductors and receptacles.

multiple receptacle: A single device with two or more receptacles.

multiwire branch circuit: A branch circuit with two or more ungrounded conductors having a voltage between them, and a grounded conductor having equal voltage between it and each ungrounded conductor while being connected to the neutral or grounded conductor of the system.

mutual induction: Voltage caused in one circuit by a change in current by another circuit. See *current* and *circuit*.

N

nominal voltage: A nominal value assigned to a circuit or system for the purpose of designating its class.

nonadjustable-trip CBs (NATCBs): Fixed CBs (circuit breakers) designed without provisions for adjusting either the ampere trip setpoint or the time-trip setpoint.

noncoincidental loads: Loads that are not on at the same time.

nonflammable liquid: A liquid that is noncombustible and does not burn when exposed to air.

nongrounding receptacles: Receptacles with two wiring slots for branch-circuit wiring systems that do not provide an equipment grounding conductor.

no-niche lighting fixture: A lighting fixture installed above or below the water without a niche.

nonlinear load: A load where the wave shape of the steady-state current does not follow the wave shape of the applied voltage.

nonmetallic extensions: Assemblies of two insulated conductors in a nonmetallic jacket or an extruded thermoplastic covering. Nonmetallic extensions are surface extensions intended for mounting directly on the surface of walls or ceilings.

nonmetallic-sheathed cable (NM): A factory assembly of two or more insulated conductors having an outer sheath of moisture-resistant, flame-retardant, nonmetallic material.

nonmetallic underground conduit with conductors (Type NUCC): A factory assembly of conductors or cables that are contained within a nonmetallic, smooth wall circular raceway.

nonmetallic wireway: A flame-retardant nonmetallic trough with a removable cover that houses and protects wires and cables laid in place after the wireway has been installed.

non-selective system: A fault on an individual branch circuit not only opens the branch-circuit overcurrent protection device, but also opens the feeder overcurrent protection device.

non-time delay fuses (NTDFs): Fuses that may detect an overcurrent and open the circuit almost instantly.

O

offset: A double bend in a raceway, with both bends containing the same number of degrees.

one-family dwelling: A dwelling with one dwelling unit.

outlet: Any point in the electrical system where current supplies utilization equipment.

outlet box: A box that houses a piece of utilization equipment.

overcurrent: Any current in excess of that for which the conductor or equipment is rated.

overlamping: Installing a lamp of a higher wattage than for which the fixture is designed.

overload: The operation of equipment in excess of normal, full-load rating, or a conductor having an excess of the rated ampacity.

oxidation: The process by which oxygen mixes with other elements and forms a rust-like material.

oxide: A thin, but highly resistive coating that forms on metal when exposed to the air.

P

panel: A collection of modules, secured together, wired, and designed to provide a field-installable unit.

panelboard: A single panel or group of assembled panels with buses and overcurrent devices, which may have switches to control light, heat, or power circuits.

panic hardware: Door hardware designed to open easily in an emergency situation.

parallel circuit: A circuit with two or more paths for current to flow. See *circuit* and *current*.

parallel conductors: Two or more conductors that are electrically connected at both ends to form a single conductor.

pendants: Hanging light fixtures that use flexible cords to support the lampholder.

permanently-connected appliance: A hard-wired appliance that is not cord-and-plug connected.

phase converter: An electrical device that converts 1ϕ power to 3ϕ power.

phase-to-ground voltage: The difference of potential between a phase conductor and ground.

phase-to-phase voltage: The maximum voltage between any two phases of an electrical distribution system.

photovoltaic output circuit: Conductors between photovoltaic source circuits and the inverter or DC utilization equipment.

photovoltaic power source: One or more arrays that generate DC power at system voltage and current.

photovoltaic source circuit: Conductors between modules and from modules to common junction point(s) of the DC system.

pilot device: A sensing device that controls the motor controller.

place of assembly: A building, structure, or portion of a building designed or intended for use by 100 or more persons.

plug fuse: A fuse that uses a metallic strip that melts when a predetermined amount of current flows through it.

potential transformer: A transformer that steps down higher voltages while allowing the voltage of the secondary to remain fairly constant from no-load to full-load conditions.

power: The rate of doing work or using energy. See *energy*.

power and control tray cable (Type TC cable): A factory-assembled cable consisting of one or more insulated copper, aluminum, or copper-clad aluminum conductors.

power factor (PF): The ratio of true power used in an AC circuit to apparent power delivered to the circuit. See *true power, apparent power,* and *circuit.*

power panelboard: A panelboard with no more than 10% of its total overcurrent devices protecting lighting and appliance branch circuits.

premises wiring: Basically all interior and exterior wiring installed on the load side of the service point or the source of a separately derived system.

pull box: A box used as a point to pull or feed electrical conductors into the raceway system.

purged and pressurized: A hazardous location protection technique that provides protection through a process that involves purging an enclosure by supplying it with a protective gas to prevent the entrance of a flammable gas or vapor.

Q

qualified person: A person who has knowledge and skills related to the construction and operation of electrical equipment and has received appropriate safety training.

R

raceway: A metal or nonmetallic enclosed channel for conductors.

raceway system: An enclosed channel of metal or nonmetallic materials used to contain the wires or cables of an electrical system.

readily accessible: Capable of being reached quickly.

receptacle: A contact device installed at outlets for the connection of cord-connected electrical equipment.

receptacle outlet: An outlet that provides power for cord-and-plug-connected equipment.

reciprocal: The inverse relationship of two numbers. See *inverse.*

recreational vehicle: A vehicular type unit that is self-propelled or is mounted on or pulled by another vehicle and is primarily designed as temporary living quarters for camping, travel, or recreational use.

redundant grounding: Grounding with two separate grounding paths.

resistance: The opposition to the flow of electrons. See *electron.*

resistance heating element: A specific element to generate heat that is embedded in or fastened to the surface.

rigid metal conduit (RMC): A threadable raceway generally made of steel or aluminum designed for physical protection of conductors and cables.

rigid nonmetallic conduit (RNC): A cross-sectional raceway of suitable nonmetallic material that is resistant to moisture and chemical atmospheres.

S

selective system: A fault on an individual branch circuit that opens only the branch-circuit overcurrent protective device and does not affect the feeder overcurrent protection device.

self-grounding receptacles: Grounding type receptacles that utilize a pressure clip around the 6–32 mounting screw to ensure good electrical contact between the receptacle yoke and the outlet box.

separately-derived system: A system that supplies a premises with electrical power derived or taken from storage batteries, solar photovoltaic systems, generators, transformers, or converter windings.

series circuit: A circuit with only one path for current to flow. See *circuit* and *current.*

service: The electrical supply, in the form of conductors and equipment, that provides electrical power to the building or structure.

service conductors: The conductors from the service point or other source of power to the service disconnecting means.

service drop: The conductors that extend from the overhead utility supply system to the service-entrance conductors at the building or structure.

service-entrance cable (SE): A single or multiconductor assembly with or without an overall covering.

service-entrance conductors—overhead systems: Conductors that connect the service equipment for the building or structure with the electrical utility supply conductors.

service-entrance conductors—underground systems: Conductors that connect the service equipment with the service lateral.

service equipment: All of the necessary equipment to control the supply of electrical power to a building or a structure.

service lateral: The underground service conductors that connect the utility's electrical distribution system with the service-entrance conductors.

service mast: An assembly consisting of a service raceway, guy wires or braces, service head, and any fittings necessary for the support of service-drop conductors.

service point: The point of connection between the local electrical utility company and the premises wiring of the building or structure.

short circuit: The unintentional connection of two ungrounded conductors that have a potential difference between them. The condition that occurs when two ungrounded conductors (hot wires), or an ungrounded and a grounded conductor of a 1ϕ circuit, come in contact with each other.

single receptacle: A single contact device with no other contact device on the same yoke.

skeleton tubing: Neon tubing that is the sign of outline lighting. It does not contain, nor is attached, to a sign body or enclosure.

solar cell: A basic photovoltaic device that generates electricity when exposed to light.

solar photovoltaic system: The system used to convert solar energy into electrical energy suitable for connection to a utilization load.

special permission: The written approval of the authority having jurisdiction.

step-down transformer: A transformer with more windings in the primary winding, which results in a load that is less than the applied voltage.

step-up transformer: A transformer with more windings in the secondary winding, which results in a load voltage that is greater than the applied voltage.

strut-type channel raceway: A surface raceway formed of moisture-resistant and corrosion-resistant metal.

supervised installation: An electrical installation in which the conditions of maintenance are such that only qualified persons monitor or service the electrical equipment.

surface raceway: An enclosed channel for conductors that is attached to a surface.

switch: A device, with a current and voltage rating, used to open or close an electrical circuit.

switchboard: A single panel or group of assembled panels with buses, overcurrent devices, and instruments.

system bonding jumper: The bonding jumper that is used to connect the grounded circuit conductor and the equipment grounding conductor at a separately derived system.

T

temperature: A measurement of the intensity of heat.

temperature rise: The amount of heat that an electrical component produces above the ambient temperature.

thermally protected: Designed with an internal thermal protective device that senses excessive operating temperatures and opens the supply circuit to the fixtures.

time delay fuses (TDFs): Fuses that may detect and remove a short circuit almost instantly, but allow small overloads to exist for a short period of time.

torque: A turning or twisting force, typically measured in foot-pounds (ft-lb).

transformer: A device that converts electrical power at one voltage or current to another voltage or current.

travel trailer: A vehicle that is mounted on wheels, has a trailer area less than 320 sq ft (excluding wardrobes, closets, cabinets, kitchen units, fixtures, etc.), is of such size and weight that a special highway use permit is not required, and is designed as temporary living quarters while camping or traveling.

true power: The actual power used in an electrical circuit. See *power*.

two-family dwelling: A dwelling with two dwelling units.

Type I building: A building in which all structural members (walls, columns, beams, girders, trusses, floors, and roofs) are constructed of approved noncombustible or limited-combustible materials; has a fire resistance rating of 0 hr to 4 hr.

Type II building: A building that does not qualify as Type I construction in which the structural members (walls, columns, beams, girders, trusses, arches, floors, roofs, etc.) are constructed of approved noncombustible or limited-combustible materials; has a fire resistance rating of 0 hr to 2 hr.

Type S fuse: A plug fuse that incorporates a screw and adapter configuration that is not interchangeable with fuses of another ampere rating.

U

underground feeder and branch-circuit cable (Type UF cable): A factory assembly of one or more insulated conductors contained within an overall covering of nonmetallic material that is suitable for direct burial applications.

unfinished basement: The portion of area of a basement that is not intended as a habitable room, but is limited to storage areas, work areas, etc.

unit switch: A switch designed to control a specific unit load.

USE: An underground service-entrance cable with a moisture-resistant covering that is not flame-resistant.

utilization equipment: Equipment that utilizes electrical energy for electronic, electromechanical, chemical, heating, lighting, or similar purposes.

V

voltage: The amount of electrical pressure in a circuit.

voltage drop: Voltage that is lost due to the resistance of conductors.

voltage-to-ground: The difference of potential between a given conductor and ground.

W

wet location: Any location in which a conductor is subjected to excessive moisture or saturation from any type of liquid or water.

wet-niche lighting fixture: A lighting fixture installed in a forming shell and completely surrounded by water.

wireway: A metallic or nonmetallic trough with a hinged or removable cover designed to house and protect conductors and cables.

USING THE *JOURNEYMAN ELECTRICIAN'S EXAM WORKBOOK* CD-ROM

Before removing the CD-ROM from the protective sleeve, please note that the book cannot be returned for refund or credit if the CD-ROM sleeve seal is broken.

System Requirements

The *Journeyman Electrician's Exam Workbook* CD-ROM is designed to work best on a computer meeting the following hardware/software requirements:

- Intel® Pentium® III (or equivalent) processor
- Microsoft® Windows Vista™, Windows XP®, Windows 2000®, or Windows NT® operating system
- 256 MB of available RAM
- 90 MB of available hard-disk space
- 800 × 600 monitor resolution
- Sound output capability and speakers
- CD-ROM drive
- Microsoft® Internet Explorer 5.5, Firefox 1.0, or Netscape® 7.1 web browser and Internet connection required for Internet links

Opening Files

Insert the CD-ROM into the computer CD-ROM drive. Within a few seconds, the home screen will be displayed allowing access to all features of the CD-ROM. Information about the usage of the CD-ROM can be accessed by clicking on USING THIS CD-ROM. The Quick Quizzes®, Illustrated Glossary, Media Clips, and ATPeResources.com can be accessed by clicking on the appropriate button on the home screen. Clicking on the American Tech web site button (www.go2atp.com) accesses information on related educational products. Unauthorized reproduction of the material on this CD-ROM is strictly prohibited.

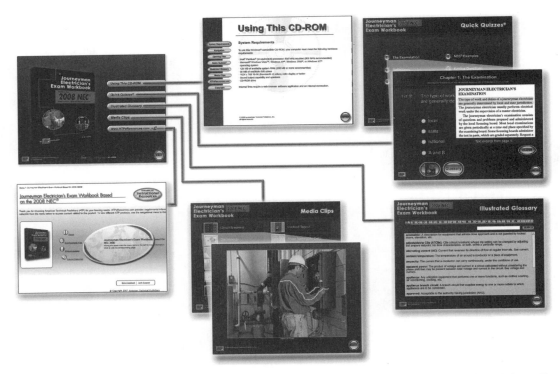